MZ Chinese Textbook Rev
and
SAT & AP Test Preparatio
(SAT & AP 題型總複習)
Level 5

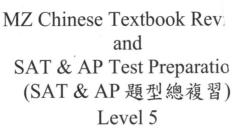

目 錄

MZ Chinese Textbook Review
and
SAT & AP Test Preparation
(SAT & AP 题型总复习)
Level 5

目 录

MZ Chinese Textbook Review
and
SAT & AP Test Preparation
(SAT & AP 題型總複習)
Level 5
主編 許笑濃

暑假就要來了! 學生對於暑假總是充滿了夢想般的期待。然而學生若在暑假期間荒廢了課業,在新學年開始時,則會出現 "summer learning loss" 的後果,特別是語文課業的倒退至少三到五個月。但學生若能在暑假每日預留一小段時間來練習,學生的課業不但會不倒退,反而能提昇到更高的層次(Paechter et al.2015)。因此之故,美洲華語決定為學生編寫一套合乎學生需求的暑假作業。

怎樣才是合乎學生需求的暑假作業呢? 筆者認為須達到以下幾點: 1. 具有吸引學生做作業的實質目標。2. 有新鮮感,與家庭作業(homework)形態不同。3. 貼近生活,應由課業範圍適度延伸,讓學生覺得有挑戰性。4. 分段量少,讓學生留有大量時間休閒玩樂或參加暑期活動。5. 提供輔助工具和標準答案,讓學生勿須尋求協助就能完成作業。經過數月的努力,今已完成了美洲華語第五冊、第六冊和第七冊暑假作業的編寫,並將於 2016 年5 月出版。

每冊作業以課為單位,每課 12 頁,每課作業分四部分,預計學生可以在 1.5 小時至2.5 小時之內完成。

一. SAT 題型部分:聽力(10題) 、語法(18題) 、閱讀(10題)。提供 CD 片錄音及標準答案。

美洲華語豐富的課文、故事內容及語法點,運用於 SAT 的聽力、語法及閱讀題型之中。讓學生在做 SAT 中文測驗練習時,同時完整地複習了本冊的課業。為了鼓勵學生不依賴注音或拼音,我們把 SAT 中文測驗語法部分的注音/拼音部分移到網上備載。

二. AP 題型部分: email 回函(1題)、看四幅圖寫故事(1題)。提供 CD 片錄音。

這是 AP 寫作部分的題型,考試時須用中文打字回答。AP 測驗和 SAT 測驗都有聽力及閱讀部分,這裡就不再重複。

三. 成語/常用詞語部分:成語選擇填充(4-6題)。提供 CD 片錄音及標準答案。

成語/常用詞語言簡意賅,是日常生活中的常用語。成語/常用詞語最有效的學習方法就是與課文結合,學起來有事半功倍的效果。題材來自本冊課文/故事,學生選擇適當的成語填入句子中。**美洲華語鼓勵老師在課堂上順便教成語/常用詞語,複習時更能加深印象。**

四. 生字詞部分:生字詞練習雖然是基本功,但暑期作業不用抄寫,只需了解英文意思後,寫出中文字詞。

暑假作業的完成有賴家長的關心和鼓勵。做作業須有持續性,最好分成兩天到四天分段完成一課,切勿積壓。暑假是加強學生語文技能的最佳時機,我們期盼這本作業能幫助學生百尺竿頭,更進一步。

寫於 2016-4-5 加州橙縣

MZ Chinese Textbook Review
and
SAT & AP Test Preparation
(SAT & AP 题型总复习)
Level 5
主编 许笑浓

　　暑假就要来了! 学生对于暑假总是充满了梦想般的期待。然而学生若在暑假期间荒废了课业，在新学年开始时，则会出现"summer learning loss"的后果，特别是语文课业的倒退至少三到五个月。但学生若能在暑假每日预留一小段时间来练习，学生的课业不但会不倒退，反而能提升到更高的层次（Paechter et al.2015）。因此之故，美洲华语决定为学生编写一套合乎学生需求的暑假作业。

　　怎样才是合乎学生需求的暑假作业呢? 笔者认为须达到以下几点: 1. 具有吸引学生做作业的实质目标。2. 有新鲜感，与家庭作业（ homework ）形态不同。3. 贴近生活，应由课业范围适度延伸，让学生觉得有挑战性。4. 分段量少，让学生留有大量时间休闲玩乐或参加暑期活动。5. 提供辅助工具和标准答案，让学生勿须寻求协助就能完成作业。经过数月的努力，今已完成了美洲华语第五册、第六册和第七册暑假作业的编写，并将于 2016 年 5 月出版。

　　每册作业以课为单位，每课 12 页，每课作业分四部分，预计学生可以在 1.5 小时至 2.5 小时之内完成。

　　一. SAT 题型部分: 听力(10题)、语法(18题)、阅读(10题)。提供 CD 片录音及标准答案。

　　美洲华语丰富的课文、故事内容及语法点，运用于 SAT 的听力、语法及阅读题型之中。让学生在做 SAT 中文测验练习时，同时完整地复习了本册的课业。为了鼓励学生不依赖注音或拼音，我们把 SAT 中文测验语法部分的注音/拼音部分移到网上备载。

　　二. A P 题型部分: email 回函(1题)。提供 CD 片录音。

　　这是 AP 写作部分的题型，考试时须用中文打字回答。AP 测验和 SAT 测验都有听力及阅读部分，这里就不再重复。

　　三. 成语/常用词语部分: 成语选择填充(4-6题)。提供 CD 片录音及标准答案。

　　成语/常用词语言简意赅，是日常生活中的常用语。成语/常用词语最有效的学习方法就是与课文结合，学起来有事半功倍的效果。题材来自本册课文/故事，学生选择适当的成语填入句子中。**美洲华语鼓励老师在课堂上顺便教成语/常用词语，复习时更能加深印象。**

　　四. 生字词部分: 生字词练习虽然是基本功，但暑期作业不用抄写，只需了解英文意思后，写出中文字词。

　　暑假作业的完成有赖家长的关心和鼓励。做作业须有持续性，最好分成两天到四天分段完成一课，切勿积压。暑假是加强学生语文技能的最佳时机，我们期盼这本作业能帮助学生百尺竿头，更进一步。

写于 2016-4-5 加州橙县

INTRODUCTION

Summer vacation is just around the corner! Students can't wait for a relaxing summer break full of fun, enjoyment, and new experiences. However, a nonacademic summer can cause students to digress two to three months in their academic skills. Thirty minutes set aside daily can help students close learning gaps and perform at higher levels during the upcoming school year. Summer is an ideal time for students of all ages to strengthen their academic skills while still having plenty of time left over for summer activities.

Designed with this in mind, our homework series offers the following features:

- Homework assignments that have students pursue meaningful objectives. We have designed the assignments to follow the format of questions commonly tested on Advanced Placement and SAT exams. This series therefore serves the dual purpose of providing enrichment and providing standardized exam preparation. Students will be able to gauge, track, and improve their performance using similar standards that universities employ to assess applicant competency.
- Content design that keeps the student engaged by offering a sense of variety.
- Course material that expands the scope of learning by building on real-life applications, thus challenging the student in interesting and appropriate ways.
- Study plans with a piecemeal structure that enables students to schedule homework assignments around their busy summer activities.
- Homework books with answer keys that serve as a training tool while providing valuable feedback and reinforcing student learning.

Each lesson itself is a homework unit consisting of four parts. Students should be able to complete each lesson within 1.5 to 2.5 hours.

PART I. <u>SAT-Type Questions</u>: Listening (10 questions), Grammar (18 questions), and Reading (10 questions). Answer Key and a CD-ROM with the transcript recording are included.

MZ Chinese's rich content of texts and stories, as well as grammar points, are well integrated into the practice questions in PART I. This integration enables students to thoroughly review the textbook lessons. In order to reduce the student's dependence on Phonetics and Pinyin for the Grammar section, these resources are accessible only on the MZ websites.

PART II. <u>AP-Type Questions</u>: Email response (1 question), and Story Narration (1 question). A CD-ROM with the transcript recording is included.

These is AP Type Writing. Test takers are required in Chinese to type their email responses. Further details on the instruction for AP Listening and Reading are not given here, since the SAT test has similar question types.

PART III. <u>Idioms/Frequently used phrases</u>: Cloze (4-6 questions). Answer Key and a CD-ROM with the transcript recording are included. Idioms and phrases are based on content from the texts and stories in the textbook. Students are asked to fill in the blanks with proper idioms or phrases.

PART IV. <u>New Characters and Words</u>: Summer homework does **not** require students to copy new characters and words from the textbook. Students only need to translate vocabulary phrases from English into Chinese.

Parental care and encouragement play an important role in ensuring that students consistently finish their homework assignments. We recommend that students split each lesson's homework into two to four sections so as not to feel overwhelmed. We sincerely hope that this book will help students continue to make great progress in their learning of the Chinese language.

Theresa Chao

什麼是 SAT？

　　SAT 是美國大學委員會（College Board）定期舉辦的大學入學資格考試，考試的成績是數千所大學錄取新生的重要評鑑。任何學生均可參加 SAT 的各項考試而且沒有年齡或次數的限制。學生可以考到 12 年級，然後把 SAT 的成績提交給所申請的大學。

　　SAT 測驗分為 SAT 推理測驗（SAT Reasoning Test）和 SAT 學科測驗（SAT Subject Test）。SAT 中文測驗是 SAT 學科測驗之一。中文測驗的考試日期是在每年 11 月份的第一個星期六。 SAT 中文測驗為一小時。

　　SAT 中文測驗一共 85 道選擇題，試題分三部份：聽力（30 題）、語法（25 題）、閱讀（30 題）。聽力部分：是用錄音播出，以測驗考生聽懂中文的能力。 語法部分：是用簡短的語句來測驗考生的文法及詞彙程度，包括虛詞、連接詞、量詞、動詞、副詞的正確使用。每一題分別用繁體字、簡體字、漢語拼音及注音符號列出，學生只需會其中一種就能作答。閱讀部分：題目以真實資料呈現。例如：招牌、時刻表、佈告、天氣預測、菜單、日記、便條、書信、新聞報導等等，皆與食、衣、住、行、娛樂等日常生活及中國文化有關。

　　SAT 中文測驗的難易程度為美國高中學生從零程度開始學中文，學了二至四年的程度。若以美洲華語課本為例，相當於學完第七冊至第九冊之間。

什麼是 AP？

　　AP（Advanced Placement）是高中課程中的大學先修課程。學生申請大學時所提交的 AP 課程及測驗成績為許多大學所重視，90%左右的美國、加拿大大學，以及 20 個左右其它國家的大學都承認它的學分。AP 中文測驗是大學理事會現有三十多門的 AP 學科測驗之一。任何高中生無論是否修過 AP 中文課程均可報考。考試日期是在每年 5 月份的前兩個星期，考試時間為 2 小時 15 分鐘。

　　AP 中文測驗分為兩部分，第一部分為聽力和閱讀，第二部分為口語和寫作。聽、讀部分是多項選擇題，寫作部分是在三十分鐘內寫一篇看圖敘述故事、一篇電子郵件回覆。口語部分包括模擬對話和文化介紹。AP 中文考試的內容不但要考核中國文化知識，而且測驗學生們在日常生活中語言溝通和文化知識運用的能力。 文化知識包括：節日、美食、旅遊、歷史、地理、文學、哲學、科學、藝術、風俗習慣等等。

　　AP 中文考試全部採用電腦進行，簡體字、繁體字試題都會顯示在同一屏幕上，學生可以在注音符號和漢語拼音中任選一種輸入方式。

　　AP 中文測驗的難易程度為美國大學生從零程度開始學中文，學完二學年的程度。若以美洲華語課本為例，相當於學完第八冊至第十冊之間。

有關 SAT 及 AP 的詳細資料請上網：
https://collegereadiness.collegeboard.org/sat-subject-tests
https://apstudent.collegeboard.org

什么是 SAT？

　　SAT 是美国大学委员会（College Board）定期举办的大学入学资格考试，考试的成绩是数千所大学录取新生的重要评鉴。任何学生均可参加 SAT 的各项考试而且没有年龄或次数的限制。学生可以考到 12 年级，然后把 SAT 的成绩提交给所申请的大学。

　　SAT 测验分为 SAT 推理测验（SAT Reasoning Test）和 SAT 学科测验（SAT Subject Test）。SAT 中文测验是 SAT 学科测验之一。中文测验的考试日期是在每年 11 月份的第一个星期六。SAT 中文测验为一小时。

　　SAT 中文测验一共 85 道选择题，试题分三部份：听力（30 题）、语法（25 题）、阅读（30 题）。听力部分：是用录音播出，以测验考生听懂中文的能力。语法部分：是用简短的语句来测验考生的文法及词汇程度，包括虚词、连接词、量词、动词、副词的正确使用。每一题分别用繁体字、简体字、汉语拼音及注音符号列出，学生只需会其中一种就能作答。阅读部分：题目以真实资料呈现。例如：招牌、时刻表、布告、天气预测、菜单、日记、便条、书信、新闻报导等等，皆与食、衣、住、行、娱乐等日常生活及中国文化有关。

　　SAT 中文测验的难易程度为美国高中学生从零程度开始学中文，学了二至四年的程度。若以美洲华语课本为例，相当于学完第七册至第九册之间。

什么是 AP？

　　AP (Advanced Placement) 是高中课程中的大学先修课程。学生申请大学时所提交的 AP 课程及测验成绩为许多大学所重视，90% 左右的美国、加拿大大学，以及 20 个左右其它国家的大学都承认它的学分。AP 中文测验是大学理事会现有三十多门的 AP 学科测验之一。任何高中生无论是否修过 AP 中文课程均可报考。考试日期是在每年 5 月份的前两个星期，考试时间为 2 小时 15 分钟。

　　AP 中文测验分为两部分，第一部分为听力和阅读，第二部分为口语和写作。听、读部分是多项选择题，写作部分是在三十分钟内写一篇看图叙述故事、一篇电子邮件回复。口语部分包括模拟对话和文化介绍。AP 中文考试的内容不但要考核中国文化知识，而且测验学生们在日常生活中语言沟通和文化知识运用的能力。文化知识包括：节日、美食、旅游、历史、地理、文学、哲学、科学、艺术、风俗习惯等等。

　　AP 中文考试全部采用电脑进行，简体字、繁体字试题都会显示在同一屏幕上，学生可以在注音符号和汉语拼音中任选一种输入方式。

　　AP 中文测验的难易程度为美国大学生从零程度开始学中文，学完二学年的程度。若以美洲华语课本为例，相当于学完第八册至第十册之间。

有关 SAT 及 AP 的详细资料请上网：
https://collegereadiness.collegeboard.org/sat-subject-tests
https://apstudent.collegeboard.org

I.　SAT Practice: 1. Listening (10)　2. Usage (18)　3. Reading Comprehension (10)

II.　AP Practice: 1. Writing (E-mail Response)　2. Writing (Story Narration)

III.　Idioms/Frequently Used Phrases

IV.　Vocabulary/Phrase Review

I.　SAT Practice
SECTION I　LISTENING　Approximate time – 10 minutes

PART A
Directions: In this part of the test, you will hear some short questions, statements, or commands, as well as responses, in Mandarin Chinese. Each question, statement, or command is followed by three responses, designated by letters (A), (B), and (C). You will hear the recording only one time. You will only hear, but not see, the recording materials. Therefore, you must listen very attentively. Select the best response and circle the answer.
Now listen to the recording.

Circle the answer.

Questions 1-4

1.　(A)　(B)　(C)

2.　(A)　(B)　(C)

3.　(A)　(B)　(C)

4.　(A)　(B)　(C)

PART B
Directions: You will now hear a series of short conversations. After each conversation, you will answer one or more questions about it. You will hear the conversations only once. You will only hear, but not see, the conversation materials. Therefore, you must listen very attentively. Select and circle your answer choice to each question. You will have fifteen seconds to answer each question.
Now listen to the first conversation.

Questions 5-6

5.　According to the conversation, why is it beneficial to learn Chinese?
　(A)　China has a fast-growing economy.
　(B)　Chinese is easy to learn.
　(C)　Chinese is one of the most-spoken languages in the world.

6. In the conversation, speaking Chinese is mentioned in all of the following situations EXCEPT:
   - (A) Building Chinese-US economic relationships
   - (B) Speaking Chinese with your family
   - (C) Engaging in Chinese-US politics

Questions 7-8

7. What is the main topic of this conversation?
   - (A) A play
   - (B) A book
   - (C) A TV program

8. Which of the following statements is INCORRECT?
   - (A) "Journey to the West" starts at 4:30 PM.
   - (B) "Journey to the West" is on Channel 18.
   - (C) "Journey to the West" is an animated film.

Questions 9-10

9. Which enrichment class is NOT mentioned in the conversation?
   - (A) Kung Fu class
   - (B) Chinese calligraphy
   - (C) Spanish class

10. Which of the following statements is INCORRECT?
    - (A) Students can also learn Chinese in enrichment classes.
    - (B) The teachers of enrichment classes speak both Chinese and English.
    - (C) The Chinese school has a basketball team.

SECTION II   USAGE
Suggested time – 20 minutes/Questions 11-28

Directions: This section consists of a number of incomplete sentences. Each sentence has three answer choices. Select one word or phrase to fill in the blank to make the sentence complete both structurally and logically.

The questions are presented in four different ways: traditional characters, simplified characters, pinyin romanization and the Chinese phonetic alphabet (bopomofo). Zhuyin and pinyin of each question are posted on the Meizhou Chinese website. You can also listen to the questions on your CD.

11. 她會說英語，＿＿會說西班牙語。

(A) 都
(B) 也
(C) 才

12. 妳會說幾＿＿語言？

(A) 部
(B) 件
(C) 種

13. 我每個週末＿＿上中文學校。

(A) 又
(B) 可
(C) 都

14. 青青很和氣，＿＿大家都喜歡她。
(A) 所以
(B) 可是
(C) 因為

15. 小孩子學語言＿＿＿大人來得容易。
(A) 給
(B) 比
(C) 有

16. 她＿＿＿＿，就把這件事說明白了。
(A) 自言自語
(B) 三言兩語
(C) 一言為定

11. 她会说英语，＿＿会说西班牙语。

(A) 都
(B) 也
(C) 才

12. 妳会说几＿＿语言？

(A) 部
(B) 件
(C) 种

13. 我每个周末＿＿上中文学校。

(A) 又
(B) 可
(C) 都

14. 青青很和气，＿＿大家都喜欢她。
(A) 所以
(B) 可是
(C) 因为

15. 小孩子学语言＿＿＿大人来得容易。
(A) 给
(B) 比
(C) 有

16. 她＿＿＿＿，就把这件事说明白了。
(A) 自言自语
(B) 三言两语
(C) 一言为定

17. _____哪種零食吃多了___不好。
    (A) 不論…都
    (B) 如果…就
    (C) 可是…還

18. 昨天我和哥哥去看了一____電影。
    (A) 套
    (B) 場
    (C) 個

19. 爸爸，你是_____認識媽媽的？
    (A) 這麼
    (B) 怎麼
    (C) 這樣

20. 他____從學校回來___去睡覺了。
    (A) 沒…就
    (B) 還…就
    (C) 才…就

21. 我___書包了，可能丟了。
    (A) 找不到
    (B) 找得到
    (C) 不找到

22. 我們第一次見面，就_____了一個
    笑話。
    (A) 吵
    (B) 叫
    (C) 鬧

17. _____哪种零食吃多了___不好。
    (A) 不论…都
    (B) 如果…就
    (C) 可是…还

18. 昨天我和哥哥去看了一____电影。
    (A) 套
    (B) 场
    (C) 个

19. 爸爸，你是_____认识妈妈的？
    (A) 这么
    (B) 怎么
    (C) 这样

20. 他____从学校回来___去睡觉了。
    (A) 没…就
    (B) 还…就
    (C) 才…就

21. 我___书包了，可能丢了。
    (A) 找不到
    (B) 找得到
    (C) 不找到

22. 我们第一次见面，就_____了一个
    笑话。
    (A) 吵
    (B) 叫
    (C) 闹

23. 你會____西班牙語說這句話嗎？
    (A) 拿
    (B) 用
    (C) 把

24. 每天___有電視看，我___很高興了。
    (A) 只要…就
    (B) 如果…不
    (C) 凡是…不

25. 她發現自己說錯話了，___說對不起。
    (A) 連接
    (B) 一連
    (C) 連忙

26. 青青的爸爸會說中文，____說得
    很好。
    (A) 還是
    (B) 並且
    (C) 可是

27. 別走!別走!我的故事___沒講完呢!
    (A) 還
    (B) 給
    (C) 又

28. 這件事_____。
    (A) 等放假以後再說吧
    (B) 再說吧等放假以後
    (C) 以後再說吧等放假

23. 你会____西班牙语说这句话吗？
    (A) 拿
    (B) 用
    (C) 把

24. 每天___有电视看，我___很高兴了。
    (A) 只要…就
    (B) 如果…不
    (C) 凡是…不

25. 她发现自己说错话了，___说对不起。
    (A) 连接
    (B) 一连
    (C) 连忙

26. 青青的爸爸会说中文，____说得
    很好。
    (A) 还是
    (B) 并且
    (C) 可是

27. 别走!别走!我的故事___没讲完呢!
    (A) 还
    (B) 给
    (C) 又

28. 这件事_____。
    (A) 等放假以后再说吧
    (B) 再说吧等放假以后
    (C) 以后再说吧等放假

SECTION III   READING COMPREHENSION
Suggested time – 20 minutes/ Questions 29 – 38

Directions: Read the following texts carefully. Each is followed by one or more questions or incomplete statements. Circle the best answer according to the text.

Question 29

親愛的小華：
　　我剛看完了你借我的那本中文故事書，很有趣。明天帶到學校還你，謝謝！
　　　　　　　童童 上

Question 29

亲爱的小华：
　　我刚看完了你借我的那本中文故事书，很有趣。明天带到学校还你，谢谢！
　　　　　　　童童 上

29. What type of book did Tong-Tong borrow from Xiao-Hua?

(A) An interesting travel book

(B) A Chinese comedy book

(C) A Chinese story book

Questions 30-31

青青全家都愛看「每日一字」這個電視節目。「每日一字」就是每天介紹一個中文字的正確發音、部首、筆畫和字的意思。這個節目很短，只有五分鐘，看的人卻很多。

Questions 30-31

青青全家都爱看"每日一字"这个电视节目。"每日一字"就是每天介绍一个中文字的正确发音、部首、笔画和字的意思。这个节目很短，只有五分钟，看的人却很多。

30. Which of the following is NOT mentioned in this TV program?

(A) Pronunciation and radicals of Chinese characters

(B) Chinese conversation

(C) Strokes and meanings of Chinese characters

31. Which of the following statements is INCORRECT?

(A) Not many people like this TV program.

(B) This TV program introduces one character a day.

(C) This is a very short program.

Questions 32-34

```
    園林電視台兒童節目表

3:30～4:00 PM  西遊記

4:00～4:10 PM  每日新聞

4:10～4:45 PM  成語故事

4:45～4:50 PM  每日一字

4:50～5:20 PM  大自然教室
```

32. What time would you turn on the TV to learn a Chinese character?

   (A)   4:50 PM
   (B)   4:10 PM
   (C)   4:45 PM

33. Which program is on air between 4:00PM and 4:10 PM?

   (A)   Journey to the West
   (B)   Children's English
   (C)   Daily News

Questions 32-34

```
    园林电视台儿童节目表

3:30～4:00 PM  西游记

4:00～4:10 PM  每日新闻

4:10～4:45 PM  成语故事

4:45～4:50 PM  每日一字

4:50～5:20 PM  大自然教室
```

34. What time would you turn on the TV to learn Chinese idioms?

   (A)   4:10 PM
   (B)   4:50 PM
   (C)   3:30 PM

Questions 35-36

```
        中文電影日
影片：我的父親母親
主演：章子怡、孫紅雷
放映日期：10 月 10 日
第一場：下午四點半
第二場：下午七點半
地點：園林中學大禮堂
票價：成人：10 元  學生：5 元
```

Questions 35-36

```
        中文电影日
影片：我的父亲母亲
主演：章子怡、孙红雷
放映日期：10 月 10 日
第一场：下午四点半
第二场：下午七点半
地点：园林中学大礼堂
票价：成人：10 元  学生：5 元
```

35. Which of the following statements is INCORRECT?

    (A) There are two TV shows every day.

    (B) The title of the movie is "My Father and Mother".

    (C) The movie will be played in the school auditorium.

36. Qing Qing and her parents will go to the movie together. What is the total cost of their tickets?

    (A) $20

    (B) $25

    (C) $15

Questions 37-38

Questions 37-38

親愛的媽媽，

　　剛剛排隊買電影票的時候，一個黑人女孩排在我前面，我用中文跟青青說：「你看，前面的女孩很漂亮。」沒想到那女孩回頭用中文說：「謝謝你！」嚇了我一跳！我本來想說：「可惜她有點胖。」還好我沒說。

明明上

亲爱的妈妈，

　　刚刚排队买电影票的时候，一个黑人女孩排在我前面，我用中文跟青青说："你看，前面的女孩很漂亮。"没想到那女孩回头用中文说："谢谢你！"吓了我一跳！我本来想说："可惜她有点胖。"还好我没说。

明明上

37. Why was Ming Ming startled after the girl spoke to her?

    (A) The girl spoke Chinese.

    (B) The girl was very rude.

    (C) The girl took Ming Ming's ticket.

38. Which of the following statements is true?

    (A) Ming Ming said that the girl was a little chubby.

    (B) Ming Ming said that the girl was rude.

    (C) Ming Ming said that the girl was pretty.

1.　Writing (E-mail Response)

Question 1 of 2: Read this e-mail from a friend and then type a response.

發件人:王明

郵件主題:請幫忙

　　我很想學中文,卻不知道要去哪裡學。聽說你每個週末都去中文學校。你能講講你的中文學校嗎?

謝謝!

发件人: 王明

邮件主题: 请帮忙

　　我很想学中文,却不知道要去哪里学。听说你每个周末都去中文学校。你能讲讲你的中文学校吗?

谢谢!

2.　Writing (Story Narration)

Question 2 of 2: The four pictures below present a story. Imagine you are writing this story to a friend. Narrate the complete story as shown in the pictures. Give your story a beginning, a middle, and an end. Please write the story on a separate sheet of paper or type it down on a computer.

III. Idioms/Frequently Used Phrases (Traditional)

You can listen to idioms, phrases, and questions on your CD.

悶ㄇㄣˋ悶ㄇㄣˋ不ㄅㄨˋ樂ㄌㄜˋ	mèn mèn bú lè	sullenly
三ㄙㄢ言ㄧㄢˊ兩ㄌㄧㄤˇ語ㄩˇ	sān yán liǎng yǔ	a few words
笑ㄒㄧㄠˋ口ㄎㄡˇ常ㄔㄤˊ開ㄎㄞ	xiào kǒu cháng kāi	always smile
字ㄗˋ正ㄓㄥˋ腔ㄑㄧㄤ圓ㄩㄢˊ	zì zhèng qiāng yuán	correct pronunciation with perfect tone
拖ㄊㄨㄛ拖ㄊㄨㄛ拉ㄌㄚ拉ㄌㄚ	tuō tuō lā lā	being sluggish; dawdling

1. Maria 是個＿＿＿＿＿＿＿＿、快快樂樂的女孩。

2. Maria 最近心情不好，常常＿＿＿＿＿＿＿。

3. 青青的爸爸＿＿＿＿＿＿＿就把學三種語言的重要性說清楚了。

4. 青青的中文很好，她的發音標準，說起話來＿＿＿＿＿＿＿。

5. 青青做作業很少＿＿＿＿＿＿＿，所以很快就做完了。

III. Idioms/Frequently Used Phrases (Simplified)

You can listen to idioms, phrases, and questions on your CD.

闷闷不乐	mèn mèn bú lè	sullenly
三言两语	sān yán liǎng yǔ	a few words
笑口常开	xiào kǒu cháng kāi	always smile
字正腔圆	zì zhèng qiāng yuán	correct pronunciation with perfect tone
拖拖拉拉	tuō tuō lā lā	being sluggish; dawdling

1. Maria 是个_____、快快乐乐的女孩。

2. Maria 最近心情不好，常常_____。

3. 青青的爸爸_____就把学三种语言的重要性说清楚了。

4. 青青的中文很好，她的发音标准，说起话来_____。

5. 青青做作业很少_____，所以很快就做完了。

IV. Vocabulary/Phrase Review

Please translate the following words/phrases into Chinese.

Lesson 1: (based on the text book   p.126)

English	Chinese	English	Chinese
father		to treasure; to cherish	
mother		and; also; besides; furthermore	
dear; beloved		movie	
Spain		children	
sufficient		to pay attention; to watch out for	
language			
regardless of; no matter what			
future			
to develop; to expand			
to tolerate; to permit; to allow			
easy; simple			

美洲華語第五冊第二課

課文：井底之蛙

故事：「故」事「今」說

美洲华语第五册第二课

课文：井底之蛙

故事："故"事"今"说

I.   SAT Practice: 1. Listening (10) 2. Usage (18) 3. Reading Comprehension (10)

II.   AP Practice: 1. Writing (E-mail Response) 2. Writing (Story Narration)

III. Idioms/Frequently Used Phrases

IV.   Vocabulary/Phrase Review

I.   SAT Practice
SECTION I   LISTENING   Approximate time – 10 minutes

PART A
Directions: In this part of the test, you will hear some short questions, statements, or commands, as well as responses, in Mandarin Chinese. Each question, statement, or command is followed by three responses, designated by letters (A), (B), and (C). You will hear the recording only one time. You will only hear, but not see, the recording materials. Therefore, you must listen very attentively. Select the best response and circle the answer.
Now listen to the recording.

Circle the answer.

Questions 1-4

1.   (A)   (B)   (C)

2.   (A)   (B)   (C)

3.   (A)   (B)   (C)

4.   (A)   (B)   (C)

PART B
Directions: You will now hear a series of short conversations. After each conversation, you will answer one or more questions about it. You will hear the conversations only once. You will only hear, but not see, the conversation materials. Therefore, you must listen very attentively. Select and circle your answer choice to each question. You will have fifteen seconds to answer each question.
Now listen to the first conversation.

Question 5

5.   According to the conversation, which of the following is NOT a recommended place to buy newspapers?

(A) Bookstore

(B) Supermarket

(C) Drugstore

Questions 6-7

6.   According to the conversation, who visited the Great Wall?

(A) Only the man

(B) Both the man and the woman

(C) Only the woman

7. Which of the following statements is CORRECT?
    (A) The woman went to Beijing two years ago.
    (B) It takes two hours to walk from Beijing to the Great Wall.
    (C) The Great Wall is made of big stones.

Question 8

8. What is the color of the Golden Gate Bridge ~~under the reflection of sun~~ on ~~the sea~~?
    (A) Gold
    (B) Orange red
    (C) Red

Questions 9-10

9. What happened to the woman?
    (A) She had chickenpox.
    (B) She had an allergy.
    (C) She had acne.

10. According to the doctor, how should she take the medicine?
    (A) Take three pills every time
    (B) Take once every three days
    (C) Take three times a day

SECTION II   USAGE
Suggested time – 20 minutes/Questions 11-28

Directions: This section consists of a number of incomplete sentences. Each sentence has three answer choices. Select one word or phrase to fill in the blank to make the sentence complete both structurally and logically.

The questions are presented in four different ways: traditional characters, simplified characters, pinyin romanization and the Chinese phonetic alphabet (bopomofo). Zhuyin and pinyin of each question are posted on the Meizhou Chinese website. You can also listen to the questions on your CD.

11. 我家住___園林市。

(A) 著
(B) 到
(C) 在

12. 快考試了，___不用功就來不及了。

(A) 再
(B) 又
(C) 都

13. 小狗____跑出去了。

(A) 在
(B) 將
(C) 又

14. 請____書還給我。
(A) 把
(B) 給
(C) 要

15. ____你想吃紅燒雞，___一定要去
這家飯館。
(A) 如果…然後
(B) 如果…就
(C) 使得…就

16. 井底之蛙____井底就是整個世界。
(A) 因為
(B) 以為
(C) 因此

11. 我家住___园林市。

(A) 着
(B) 到
(C) 在

12. 快考试了，___不用功就来不及了。

(A) 再
(B) 又
(C) 都

13. 小狗____跑出去了。

(A) 在
(B) 将
(C) 又

14. 请____书还给我。
(A) 把
(B) 给
(C) 要

15. ____你想吃红烧鸡，___一定要去
这家饭馆。
(A) 如果…然后
(B) 如果…就
(C) 使得…就

16. 井底之蛙____井底就是整个世界。
(A) 因为
(B) 以为
(C) 因此

17. 一個人知道的不多，卻很自滿，

　　就像是____。

(A) 見多識廣

(B) 井底之蛙

(C) 舉一反三

18. 放學＿＿，我們去游泳好嗎?

(A) 以後

(B) 後面

(C) 後來

19. 老師問:「有____要去洗手間?」

(A) 不

(B) 沒

(C) 誰

20. 這___報紙是今天的嗎?

(A) 把

(B) 個

(C) 份

21. 你看! 樹上有一____大鳥。

(A) 隻

(B) 個

(C) 頭

22. 他____一進門____喊肚子餓。

(A) 就…才

(B) 剛…就

(C) 才…還

17. 一个人知道的不多，却很自满，

　　就像是____。

(A) 见多识广

(B) 井底之蛙

(C) 举一反三

18. 放学＿＿，我们去游泳好吗?

(A) 以后

(B) 后面

(C) 后来

19. 老师问: "有____要去洗手间?"

(A) 不

(B) 没

(C) 谁

20. 这___报纸是今天的吗?

(A) 把

(B) 个

(C) 份

21. 你看! 树上有一____大鸟。

(A) 只

(B) 个

(C) 头

22. 他____一进门____喊肚子饿。

(A) 就…才

(B) 刚…就

(C) 才…还

23. 友友，今天___得怎麼樣？
   (A) 過
   (B) 來
   (C) 去

24. 醫生，他__了什麼病？
   (A) 的
   (B) 得
   (C) 有

25. 他沒學過畫畫，____他畫得很好。
   (A) 所以
   (B) 當然
   (C) 但是

26. 我長大以後要____老師。
   (A) 成
   (B) 扮
   (C) 當

27. _____吃飯_____看報紙的習慣不好。
   (A) 一次…一次
   (B) 一邊…一邊
   (C) 旁邊…旁邊

28. 他的_____。
   (A) 已經中文很好了
   (B) 中文很好了已經
   (C) 中文已經很好了

23. 友友，今天___得怎么样？
   (A) 过
   (B) 来
   (C) 去

24. 医生，他__了什么病？
   (A) 的
   (B) 得
   (C) 有

25. 他没学过画画，____他画得很好。
   (A) 所以
   (B) 当然
   (C) 但是

26. 我长大以后要____老师。
   (A) 成
   (B) 扮
   (C) 当

27. _____吃饭_____看报纸的习惯不好。
   (A) 一次…一次
   (B) 一边…一边
   (C) 旁边…旁边

28. 他的_____。
   (A) 已经中文很好了
   (B) 中文很好了已经
   (C) 中文已经很好了

SECTION III   READING COMPREHENSION
Suggested time – 20 minutes/ Questions 29 – 38

Directions: Read the following texts carefully. Each is followed by one or more questions or incomplete statements. Circle the best answer according to the text.

Question 29

金門大橋遊客中心禮品店
每日開放
早上 9 點半到下午 4 點半

Question 29

金门大桥游客中心礼品店
每日开放
早上 9 点半到下午 4 点半

29. Where should this sign be displayed in Visitor Center?

(A) Gift shop
(B) Restaurant
(C) Newspaper stand

Questions 30-31

《世界日報》
《星島日報》
每份五毛錢
請把報費放在盒子裡

Questions 30-31

《世界日报》
《星岛日报》
每份五毛钱
请把报费放在盒子里

30. How much is a newspaper?

(A) Five dollars each
(B) Five cents each
(C) Fifty cents each

31. How do you pay for the newspaper?

(A) Pay inside.
(B) Pay a cashier.
(C) Leave money in the box.

親愛的王老師：

　明明得了流感，並且發高燒，不能上課。醫生要她在家休息三天。請老師把明明的家庭作業用郵件發給我，如果有其他事情，請發郵件或是打電話給我。謝謝！

　　　　　　　　明明的母親　上

Questions 32-33

亲爱的王老师：

　明明得了流感，并且发高烧，不能上课。医生要她在家休息三天。请老师把明明的家庭作业用邮件发给我，如果有其他事情，请发邮件或是打电话给我。谢谢！

　　　　　　　　明明的母亲　上

32. Which one of the following statements is INCORRECT?

(A) Ming Ming got the flu and fever.
(B) Ming Ming will be absent for a week.
(C) Ming Ming's mother asked the teacher to email the homework to her.

33. How should the teacher contact Ming `Ming's mother if he has questions?
(A) The teacher can email her.
(B) The teacher can text her.
(C) The teacher can fax her.

Questions 34-36

親愛的小華：

　你好嗎?我和幾個朋友出去旅遊了半個月，昨天才到家。這次我們從美國東岸一直玩到西岸。我們去過紐約的自由女神像，去過黃石公園，還去過舊金山的中國城和金門大橋。玩得很高興。

祝你平安健康！

　　　　　　　　爺爺　字

Questions 34-36

亲爱的小华：

　你好吗?我和几个朋友出去旅游了半个月，昨天才到家。这次我们从美国东岸一直玩到西岸。我们去过纽约的自由女神像，去过黄石公园，还去过旧金山的中国城和金门大桥。玩得很高兴。

祝你平安健康！

　　　　　　　　爷爷　字

34. How long did Xiao Hua's grandfather spend on the trip?
   (A) About two weeks
   (B) About ten days
   (C) About a month

35. Where did he start the trip?
   (A) Yellowstone National park
   (B) Chinatown in San Francisco
   (C) Central Park in New York

36. Which one of the following statements is INCORRECT?
   (A) Grandfather went to see the Statue of Liberty.
   (B) Grandfather traveled from the west coast to the east coast.
   (C) Grandfather came back yesterday.

Questions 37-38

友友聽了井底之蛙的故事後，就想養一隻青蛙當寵物。爺爺告訴他：「青蛙怕冷又怕熱，而且每天還要吃小蟲或小魚，只吃活的，不吃死的。所以養青蛙很麻煩。」友友說：「那還不如養狗呢。」

Questions 37-38

友友听了井底之蛙的故事后，就想养一只青蛙当宠物。爷爷告诉他："青蛙怕冷又怕热，而且每天还要吃小虫或小鱼，只吃活的，不吃死的。所以养青蛙很麻烦。"友友说："那还不如养狗呢。"

37. According to the text, what kind of pet is NOT mentioned?
   (A) Dog
   (B) Cat
   (C) Fish

38. Which of the following statements is true?
   (A) Taking care of a pet frog is quite easy.
   (B) Frogs cannot stand very hot or very cold weather.
   (C) Frogs love to eat both live and dead bugs.

II. AP Practice
1. Writing (E-mail Response)

Question 1 of 2: Read this e-mail from a friend and then type a response.

發件人：小華

郵件主題：井底之蛙

　　今天小華很不高興，因為有人說她是井底之蛙。什麼是井底之蛙呀？請你告訴我？謝謝！

发件人：小华

邮件主题：井底之蛙

　　今天小华很不高兴，因为有人说她是井底之蛙。什么是井底之蛙呀？请你告诉我？谢谢！

2. Writing (Story Narration)

Question 2 of 2: The four pictures below present a story. Imagine you are writing this story to a friend. Narrate the complete story as shown in the pictures. Give your story a beginning, a middle, and an end. Please write the story on a separate sheet of paper or type it down on a computer.

III. Idioms/Frequently Used Phrases (Traditional)

You can listen to idioms, phrases, and questions on your CD.

自大自滿	zì dà zì mǎn	egotistic and gloating
一望無際	yí wàng wú jì	stretching far off into the distance and out of sight
坐井觀天	zuò jǐng guān tiān	to view the sky from the bottom of a well; ignorant and narrow-minded
井底之蛙	jǐng dǐ zhī wā	a frog at the bottom of a well; an ignorant person
百花盛開	bǎi huā shèng kāi	hundreds of flowers are in full bloom
快快樂樂	kuài kuài lè lè	happily

1. 一隻青蛙住在井底，牠很_____，我們就叫牠

   _____。

2. 有一天，井底之蛙跳出了井口，牠發現外面是一個_____的

   寬廣世界。

3. 井底之蛙來到了一個公園，公園裡_____十分美麗，有許多

   青蛙住在這裡。

4. 於是，井底之蛙決定住下來，和大家一起_____地過日子。

5. 井底之蛙不回井底了，因為牠不想再當一個_____的井底之

   蛙。

III. Idioms/Frequently Used Phrases (Simplified)

You can listen to idioms, phrases, and questions on your CD.

自大自满	zì dà zì mǎn	egotistic and gloating
一望无际	yí wàng wú jì	stretching far off into the distance and out of sight
坐井观天	zuò jǐng guān tiān	to view the sky from the bottom of a well; ignorant and narrow-minded
井底之蛙	jǐng dǐ zhī wā	a frog at the bottom of a well; an ignorant person
百花盛开	bǎi huā shèng kāi	hundreds of flowers are in full bloom
快快乐乐	kuài kuài lè lè	happily

1. 一只青蛙住在井底，它很_____，我们就叫它

    _____。

2. 有一天，井底之蛙跳出了井口，它发现外面是一个_____的

    宽广世界。

3. 井底之蛙来到了一个公园，公园里_____十分美丽，有许多

    青蛙住在这里。

4. 于是，井底之蛙决定住下来，和大家一起_____地过日子。

5. 井底之蛙不回井底了，因为它不想再当一个_____的井底之

    蛙。

IV. Vocabulary/Phrase Review

Please translate the following words/phrases into Chinese.

<u>Lesson 2:</u> (based on the text book p.126)

English	Chinese	English	Chinese
to chat; a chat		any; all	
all day long		how; (no matter) what	
newspaper		to refuse	
white paper		to study hard	
television		to learn; to study; learning	
bottom of a well			
frog at the bottom of a well			
story			
consequently; therefore			
grandfather			
in fact; actually			

美洲華語第五冊第三課

課文：萬聖節

故事：這是我自己做的

美洲华语第五册第三课

课文：万圣节

故事：这是我自己做的

I.   SAT Practice: 1. Listening (10) 2. Usage (18) 3. Reading Comprehension (10)

II. AP Practice: 1. Writing (E-mail Response) 2. Writing (Story Narration)

III. Idioms/Frequently Used Phrases

IV. Vocabulary/Phrase Review

I.   SAT Practice
SECTION I   LISTENING   Approximate time – 10 minutes

PART A
Directions: In this part of the test, you will hear some short questions, statements, or commands, as well as responses, in Mandarin Chinese. Each question, statement, or command is followed by three responses, designated by letters (A), (B), and (C). You will hear the recording only one time. You will only hear, but not see, the recording materials. Therefore, you must listen very attentively. Select the best response and circle the answer.
Now listen to the recording.

PART B
Directions: You will now hear a series of short conversations. After each conversation, you will answer one or more questions about it. You will hear the conversations only once. You will only hear, but not see, the conversation materials. Therefore, you must listen very attentively. Select and circle your answer choice to each question. You will have fifteen seconds to answer each question.
Now listen to the first conversation.

Circle the answer.

Questions 1-4

1.   (A)   (B)   (C)

2.   (A)   (B)   (C)

3.   (A)   (B)   (C)

4.   (A)   (B)   (C)

Question 5

5.   Why did they decorate the house?
(A) For Halloween
(B) For a dinner party
(C) For a surprise birthday party

Question 6

6.   What will they make this weekend?
(A) Jack-O-Lanterns
(B) Spider webs
(C) A Witch

Questions 7-8

7. According to the girl, why does she NOT recommend candy for Halloween?

   (A) Because candy is not good for your teeth.

   (B) Because candy is very costly.

   (C) Because candy may cause obesity.

8. What is their final decision for what to give out as treats?

   (A) A pencil

   (B) A red envelope with one dollar in it

   (C) A book

Questions 9-10

9. Where will they go for Trick-or-Treating?

   (A) Supermarket

   (B) Neighborhood

   (C) Shopping mall

10. Which of the following statements is INCORRECT?

   (A) It is safer to Trick or Treat in the mall.

   (B) Most stores are closed on Halloween evening.

   (C) People do not need to worry about bad weather inside a mall.

SECTION II   USAGE
Suggested time – 20 minutes/Questions 11-28

Directions: This section consists of a number of incomplete sentences. Each sentence has three answer choices. Select one word or phrase to fill in the blank to make the sentence complete both structurally and logically.

The questions are presented in four different ways: traditional characters, simplified characters, pinyin romanization and the Chinese phonetic alphabet (bopomofo). Zhuyin and pinyin of each question are posted on the Meizhou Chinese website. You can also listen to the questions on your CD.

11. 我喜歡過萬聖節，你___？

(A) 吧

(B) 嗎

(C) 呢

12. 她打扮成巫婆，我___她嚇了一跳。

(A) 被

(B) 給

(C) 把

13. _____妖魔鬼怪我們都見過，

別怕！

(A) 這麼

(B) 怎麼

(C) 什麼

14. 他常常把頭髮染成不同顏色，我們

早就____了。

(A) 奇形怪狀

(B) 見怪不怪

(C) 不聲不響

15. 別著急！我們_____快到學校了。

(A) 就

(B) 才

(C) 還

16. 兒女___孝順父母。

(A) 因此

(B) 因為

(C) 應該

11. 我喜欢过万圣节，你___？

(A) 吧

(B) 吗

(C) 呢

12. 她打扮成巫婆，我___她吓了一跳。

(A) 被

(B) 给

(C) 把

13. _____妖魔鬼怪我们都见过，

别怕！

(A) 这么

(B) 怎么

(C) 什么

14. 他常常把头发染成不同颜色，我们

早就____了。

(A) 奇形怪状

(B) 见怪不怪

(C) 不声不响

15. 别着急！我们_____快到学校了。

(A) 就

(B) 才

(C) 还

16. 儿女___孝顺父母。

(A) 因此

(B) 因为

(C) 应该

17. 今天很冷，你＿＿＿穿件外套吧。
    (A) 更加
    (B) 還是
    (C) 總是

18. 我們應該＿＿大家說明這件事。
    (A) 將
    (B) 向
    (C) 把

19. 爸爸今天買了三＿＿領帶。
    (A) 條
    (B) 個
    (C) 件

20.我先寫作業，＿＿＿＿練鋼琴。
    (A) 依然
    (B) 果然
    (C) 然後

21. 你要打扮成孫悟空＿＿豬八戒?
    (A) 還要
    (B) 還是
    (C) 還做

22. 這是誰＿＿面具?
    (A) 的
    (B) 得
    (C) 地

17. 今天很冷，你＿＿＿穿件外套吧。
    (A) 更加
    (B) 还是
    (C) 总是

18. 我们应该＿＿大家说明这件事。
    (A) 将
    (B) 向
    (C) 把

19. 爸爸今天买了三＿＿领带。
    (A) 条
    (B) 个
    (C) 件

20.我先写作业，＿＿＿＿练钢琴。
    (A) 依然
    (B) 果然
    (C) 然后

21. 你要打扮成孙悟空＿＿猪八戒?
    (A) 还要
    (B) 还是
    (C) 还做

22. 这是谁＿＿面具?
    (A) 的
    (B) 得
    (C) 地

23. 媽媽才進廚房，＿＿＿就把飯做好了。
    (A) 不一多久
    (B) 不一下兒
    (C) 不一會兒

24. 她＿＿＿了一頂紅帽子。
    (A) 戴
    (B) 穿
    (C) 圍

25. 我昨天＿＿＿找你，你去哪裡了？
    (A) 全部
    (B) 到底
    (C) 到處

26. ＿＿＿我們開一個化妝舞會，一定
    很好玩。
    (A) 如何
    (B) 如果
    (C) 任何

27. 您就是明明的媽媽＿＿＿!請進，請進。
    (A) 吧
    (B) 嗎
    (C) 呢

28. 哥哥＿＿＿＿＿＿＿＿
    (A) 幫我昨天電腦裝好了。
    (B) 昨天幫我把電腦裝好了。
    (C) 電腦幫我裝好了昨天。

23. 妈妈才进厨房，＿＿＿就把饭做好了。
    (A) 不一多久
    (B) 不一下儿
    (C) 不一会儿

24. 她＿＿＿了一顶红帽子。
    (A) 戴
    (B) 穿
    (C) 围

25. 我昨天＿＿＿找你，你去哪里了？
    (A) 全部
    (B) 到底
    (C) 到处

26. ＿＿＿我们开一个化妆舞会，一定
    很好玩。
    (A) 如何
    (B) 如果
    (C) 任何

27. 您就是明明的妈妈＿＿＿!请进，请进。
    (A) 吧
    (B) 吗
    (C) 呢

28. 哥哥＿＿＿＿＿＿＿＿
    (A) 帮我昨天电脑装好了。
    (B) 昨天帮我把电脑装好了。
    (C) 电脑帮我装好了昨天。

SECTION III   READING COMPREHENSION
Suggested time – 20 minutes/ Questions 29 – 38

Directions: Read the following texts carefully. Each is followed by one or more questions or incomplete statements. Circle the best answer according to the text.

Question 29

美美時裝店
萬聖節服裝大減價

29. Which event does this sign promote?

(A) Halloween costumes sold out

(B) New Halloween costumes available

(C) A big sale on Halloween costumes

Questions 30-31

百利農場萬聖節活動：
烤肉，要糖果，鬼屋探險，做南瓜燈籠，
萬聖節化妝比賽，兒童遊戲等。
日期：10 月 24 日下午五點到半夜
入場費：每人＄5 元

30. Where will be the Halloween party?

(A) At a playground

(B) At a farm

(C) At a park

31. Which of the following activities is NOT mentioned?

(A) Bonfire

(B) Haunted house

(C) Costume competition

Question 29

美美时装店
万圣节服装大减价

Questions 30-31

百利农场万圣节活动：
烤肉，要糖果，鬼屋探险，做南瓜灯笼，
万圣节化妆比赛，儿童游戏等。
日期：10 月 24 日下午五点到半夜
入场费：每人＄5 元

萬聖節遊行

日期：10 月 31 日

時間：上午九點到十一點半

地點：運動場

注意事項：不允許帶面具，不允許帶尖銳危險的道具。

萬圣节游行

日期：10 月 31 日

时间：上午九点到十一点半

地点：运动场

注意事项：不允许带面具，不允许带尖锐危险的道具。

32. Which event does this sign promote?

(A) A fashion show

(B) A Halloween party

(C) A Halloween parade

33. Which of the following statements is INCORRECT?

(A) Participants are allowed to wear masks.

(B) This event is being held at the schoolyard.

(C) Students cannot bring props with sharp tips or blades.

Questions 34-35

Questions 34-35

公告

萬聖節糖果捐贈活動：

　　每年的萬聖節之後，家家都有多餘的糖果，不知道如何處理。本校將收集糖果分送給附近的兒童醫院和老人院。如果你願意支持這項活動，請在十一月一日早上十點以前把糖果送到辦公室。

園林小學家長會 啟

十月二十五日

公告

万圣节糖果捐赠活动：

　　每年的万圣节之后，家家都有多余的糖果，不知道如何处理。本校将收集糖果分送给附近的儿童医院和老人院。如果你愿意支持这项活动，请在十一月一日早上十点以前把糖果送到办公室。

园林小学家长会 启

十月二十五日

34. What is this announcement for?

(A) A candy sale for boy scouts

(B) A candy donation drive

(C) A Children's Hospital fundraiser

35. Which of the following statements is correct?

(A) This event will occur on 10/25.

(B) This is a charity event.

(C) The funds from the event will be given to retirement homes.

Questions 36-38

十月二十一日　　　　　晴天

　今年學校有萬聖節遊行，友友打扮成豬八戒。他用大紙杯做鼻子，把兩塊布剪成兩個大耳朵。他穿了爸爸的睡衣，裡面放了一個枕頭當肚子。他光著腳，手裡拿著掃把，一搖一擺地走過來。同學們都說他很像豬八戒。

Questions 36-38

十月二十一日　　　　　晴天

　今年学校有万圣节游行，友友打扮成猪八戒。他用大纸杯做鼻子，把两块布剪成两个大耳朵。他穿了爸爸的睡衣，里面放了一个枕头当肚子。他光着脚，手里拿着扫把，一摇一摆地走过来。同学们都说他很像猪八戒。

36. Who does You You dress up as?

(A) Sandy

(B) Pigsy

(C) Monkey King

37. Which of the following items are NOT mentioned in the text?

(A) Clothes, pillow, cups

(B) Broom, cups, clothes

(C) Shoes, cups, pillow

38. Which of the following statements is INCORRECT?

(A) You You held a stick.

(B) You You walked with bare feet.

(C) You You wore pajamas.

AP Practice
1. Writing (E-mail Response)

Question 1 of 2: Read this e-mail from a friend and then type a response.

發件人：明明

郵件主題：萬聖節

　　今年的萬聖節，你帶著巫婆的面具來我們家要糖，我外婆嚇了一跳，她說在中國沒有這樣的節，請你告訴我，為什麼會有萬聖節？

发件人：明明

邮件主题：万圣节

　　今年的万圣节，你带着巫婆的面具来我们家要糖，我外婆吓了一跳，她说在中国没有这样的节，请你告诉我，为什么会有万圣节？

2. Writing (Story Narration)

Question 2 of 2: The four pictures below present a story. Imagine you are writing this story to a friend. Narrate the complete story as shown in the pictures. Give your story a beginning, a middle, and an end. Please write the story on a separate sheet of paper or type it down on a computer.

III. Idioms/Frequently Used Phrases (Traditional)

You can listen to idioms, phrases, and questions on your CD.

偷偷摸摸	tōu tōu mō mō	in a sneaky way
各式各樣	gè shì gè yàng	all kinds of; a variety of
歡歡喜喜	huān huān xǐ xǐ	joyfully
千奇百怪	qiān qí bǎi guài	all sorts [kinds] of strange things
挨家挨戶	āi jiā āi hù	to go from door to door

1. 很久以前，人們相信在萬聖節的晚上，鬼怪們會_____地跑出來搶東西吃。

2. 為了把鬼嚇走，人們就戴上_____的凶惡面具，在外面走來走去。

3. 後來，萬聖節成了孩子們的大節日。到了晚上，孩子們_____地穿上_____的服裝，上街要糖。

4. 他們_____地要糖吃，「不給糖，就搗蛋」就是這麼來的。

III. Idioms/Frequently Used Phrases (Simplified)

You can listen to idioms, phrases, and questions on your CD.

偷偷摸摸	tōu tōu mō mō	in a sneaky way
各式各样	gè shì gè yàng	all kinds of; a variety of
欢欢喜喜	huān huān xǐ xǐ	joyfully
千奇百怪	qiān qí bǎi guài	all sorts [kinds] of strange things
挨家挨户	āi jiā āi hù	to go from door to door

1. 很久以前，人们相信在万圣节的晚上，鬼怪们会_____地

    跑出来抢东西吃。

2. 为了把鬼吓走，人们就戴上_____的凶恶面具，在外面走来

    走去。

3. 后来，万圣节成了孩子们的大节日。到了晚上，孩子们_____

    地穿上_____的服装，上街要糖。

4. 他们_____地要糖吃，"不给糖，就捣蛋"就是这么来的。

IV. Vocabulary/Phrase Review

Please translate the following words/phrases into Chinese.

Lesson 3: (based on the text book p.126-127)

English	Chinese	English	Chinese
Halloween		should; ought to	
saint; sage		should; ought to; must	
schoolyard		white cloth	
inside the schoolyard (or school)		bed sheet	
clothes		idea; notion; plan	
put on			
to give or attend class			
to masquerade (as)			
to have a good fright			
to be frightened			
to commemorate			

美洲華語第五冊第四課
　課文:古詩二首
　故事:有獎！有獎！

美洲华语第五册第四课
　课文: 古诗二首
　故事: 有奖！有奖！

I. SAT Practice: 1. Listening (10) 2. Usage (18) 3. Reading Comprehension (10)

II. AP Practice: 1. Writing (E-mail Response) 2. Writing (Story Narration)

III. Idioms/Frequently Used Phrases

IV. Vocabulary/Phrase Review

I. SAT Practice
SECTION I LISTENING Approximate time – 10 minutes

PART A
Directions: In this part of the test, you will hear some short questions, statements, or commands, as well as responses, in Mandarin Chinese. Each question, statement, or command is followed by three responses, designated by letters (A), (B), and (C). You will hear the recording only one time. You will only hear, but not see, the recording materials. Therefore, you must listen very attentively. Select the best response and circle the answer.
Now listen to the recording.

Circle the answer.

Questions 1-4

1. (A)　(B)　(C)

2. (A)　(B)　(C)

3. (A)　(B)　(C)

4. (A)　(B)　(C)

PART B
Directions: You will now hear a series of short conversations. After each conversation, you will answer one or more questions about it. You will hear the conversations only once. You will only hear, but not see, the conversation materials. Therefore, you must listen very attentively. Select and circle your answer choice to each question. You will have fifteen seconds to answer each question.
Now listen to the first conversation.

Question 5

5. According to the girl, what is the easiest way to memorize the poem?

　(A) Using pictures as hints
　(B) Reading the poem aloud
　(C) Copying down the poem several times

Question 6

6. Why do they like this classical poem?
　(A) Because it is a popular classical poem.
　(B) Because it is short and easy to memorize.
　(C) Because it is easy to understand the meaning of the poem.

Questions 7-8

7. Which dynasty is the golden age of classical Chinese poetry?

   (A) Qin Dynasty

   (B) Tang Dynasty

   (C) Ming Dynasty

8. When is the golden age of classical Chinese poetry?

   (A) About one thousand to fifteen hundred years ago

   (B) Less than one thousand years ago

   (C) More than fifteen hundred years ago

Questions 9-10

9. What is *300 Tang Poems* ?

   (A) It is a book of Tang literature.

   (B) It is a book of Tang history.

   (C) It is a collection of Tang poems.

10. How many famous poets are featured in *300 Tang Poems*?

    (A) 77

    (B) 311

    (C) 300

SECTION II   USAGE
Suggested time – 20 minutes/Questions 11-28

Directions: This section consists of a number of incomplete sentences. Each sentence has three answer choices. Select one word or phrase to fill in the blank to make the sentence complete both structurally and logically.

The questions are presented in four different ways: traditional characters, simplified characters, pinyin romanization and the Chinese phonetic alphabet (bopomofo). Zhuyin and pinyin of each question are posted on the Meizhou Chinese website. You can also listen to the questions on your CD.

11. 今天我們學了兩＿唐詩。

    (A) 個

    (B) 首

    (C) 條

12. 醫生說，這瓶藥必須在七天＿＿＿＿

    吃完。

    (A) 之外

    (B) 之內

    (C) 之中

13. 這首詩很容易，＿＿念幾遍＿＿＿會背了。

    (A) 只要…就

    (B) 只能…就

    (C) 只好…就

14. ＿＿＿＿＿你累了，＿＿＿＿休息一會兒吧！

    (A) 突然…就

    (B) 如果…就

    (C) 如今…還

15. 老師說，你們誰有問題，現在＿＿＿＿

    問。

    (A) 可以

    (B) 可能

    (C) 可是

16. 這個巧克力蛋糕，＿＿＿很好吃喔！

    (A) 拿起來

    (B) 看起來

    (C) 說起來

11. 今天我们学了两＿唐诗。

    (A) 个

    (B) 首

    (C) 条

12. 医生说，这瓶药必须在七天＿＿＿＿

    吃完。

    (A) 之外

    (B) 之内

    (C) 之中

13. 这首诗很容易，＿＿念几遍＿＿＿会背了。

    (A) 只要…就

    (B) 只能…就

    (C) 只好…就

14. ＿＿＿＿＿你累了，＿＿＿＿休息一会儿吧！

    (A) 突然…就

    (B) 如果…就

    (C) 如今…还

15. 老师说，你们谁有问题，现在＿＿＿＿

    问。

    (A) 可以

    (B) 可能

    (C) 可是

16. 这个巧克力蛋糕，＿＿＿很好吃喔！

    (A) 拿起来

    (B) 看起来

    (C) 说起来

17. 這隻大狗看起來很兇，_____牠
    很乖。
    (A) 其中
    (B) 尤其
    (C) 其實

18. 這幾家飯館的菜都很好吃，_____這家
    最有名。
    (A) 其他
    (B) 其中
    (C) 其內

19. 你不高興，___說出來。
    (A) 就
    (B) 會
    (C) 來

20. 你說的____不錯，他真的很會唱歌。
    (A) 結果
    (B) 如果
    (C) 果然

21. 現在__不到九點鐘，你怎麼就睏了？
    (A) 還
    (B) 再
    (C) 有

22. 天氣____冷，樹葉___變紅了。
    (A) 一…一
    (B) 還…就
    (C) 一…就

17. 这只大狗看起来很凶，_____它
    很乖。
    (A) 其中
    (B) 尤其
    (C) 其实

18. 这几家饭馆的菜都很好吃，_____这家
    最有名。
    (A) 其他
    (B) 其中
    (C) 其内

19. 你不高兴，___说出来。
    (A) 就
    (B) 会
    (C) 来

20. 你说的____不错，他真的很会唱歌。
    (A) 结果
    (B) 如果
    (C) 果然

21. 现在__不到九点钟，你怎么就困了？
    (A) 还
    (B) 再
    (C) 有

22. 天气____冷，树叶___变红了。
    (A) 一…一
    (B) 还…就
    (C) 一…就

- 47 -

23. 我_____喜歡李白的詩。
    (A) 特別
    (B) 特地
    (C) 特多

24. 我_____再也沒有見過他。
    (A) 以前
    (B) 然後
    (C) 後來

25. 李白想家，___寫下了靜夜思。
    (A) 由於
    (B) 於是
    (C) 至於

26. 今天天氣很熱，明天會___熱。
    (A) 有
    (B) 又
    (C) 更

27. 他____當時的情景寫成了一首詩。
    (A) 被
    (B) 拿
    (C) 把

28. 張老師_____。
    (A) 每個人發給兩張講義
    (B) 兩張講義發給每個人
    (C) 發給每個人兩張講義

23. 我_____喜欢李白的诗。
    (A) 特别
    (B) 特地
    (C) 特多

24. 我_____再也没有见过他。
    (A) 以前
    (B) 然后
    (C) 后来

25. 李白想家，___写下了静夜思。
    (A) 由于
    (B) 于是
    (C) 至于

26. 今天天气很热，明天会___热。
    (A) 有
    (B) 又
    (C) 更

27. 他____当时的情景写成了一首诗。
    (A) 被
    (B) 拿
    (C) 把

28. 张老师_____。
    (A) 每个人发给两张讲义
    (B) 两张讲义发给每个人
    (C) 发给每个人两张讲义

SECTION III   READING COMPREHENSION

Suggested time – 20 minutes/ Questions 29 – 38

Directions: Read the following texts carefully. Each is followed by one or more questions or incomplete statements. Circle the best answer according to the text.

Question 29

《我會念古詩》

有聲學習書

中華兒童出版社

Question 29

《我会念古诗》

有声学习书

中华儿童出版社

29. Which of the following statements is true?

(A) This is a collection of clasical poems for kids.

(B) This is a story book with audio.

(C) This is a children's poetry book with audio.

Questions 30-32

中山小學五年級唐詩背誦比賽

比賽內容：以下三首，自選一首。

《靜夜思》、《春曉》、《尋隱者不遇》

獎品(禮券)：第一名: $30 第二名:$20

第三名: $10

比賽時間：12 月 5 日下午 3:00

比賽地點：學校大禮堂

請在 11 月 30 日前上網報名

網址：zhongshanschool.edu

Questions 30-32

中山小学五年级唐诗背诵比赛

比赛内容: 以下三首，自选一首。

《静夜思》、《春晓》、《寻隐者不遇》

奖品(礼券): 第一名: $30 第二名:$20

第三名: $10

比赛时间: 12 月 5 日下午 3:00

比赛地点: 学校大礼堂

请在 11 月 30 日前上网报名

网址: zhongshanschool.edu

30. What is this announcement for?

(A) A poetry acting contest

(B) A poetry writing contest

(C) A poetry recitation contest

31. What is the registration deadline?

(A) October 20th

(B) November 30th

(C) December 5th

32. Which of the following statements is true?

    (A) Winners will receive cash awards.

    (B) Students can sign up online.

    (C) Students need to recite three poems.

Questions 33-34

親愛的爸爸：

  中文學校放學後，媽媽帶我來中國城買菜了。我們會買您愛吃的春捲和豬肉餃子，另外您還想吃什麼嗎？請您告訴我。謝謝！

青青 敬上

Questions 33-34

亲爱的爸爸：

  中文学校放学后，妈妈带我来中国城买菜了。我们会买您爱吃的春卷和猪肉饺子，另外您还想吃什么吗？请您告诉我。谢谢！

青青 敬上

33. Where did Qing Qing go?

    (A) Restaurant

    (B) Shopping Mall

    (C) Chinatown

34. Which of the following statements is true?

    (A) Qing Qing's father likes to eat pork dumplings.

    (B) Qing Qing likes to eat spring rolls.

    (C) Qing Qing went shopping with her father.

Questions 35-36

親愛的青青：

  很高興你會使用手機發短信了，請你告訴媽媽，如果方便的話，請她順便買紅包袋、幾支毛筆和寫春聯的紅紙回來。謝謝！

爸爸字

Questions 35-36

亲爱的青青：

  很高兴你会使用手机发短信了，请你告诉妈妈，如果方便的话，请她顺便买红包袋、几支毛笔和写春联的红纸回来。谢谢！

爸爸字

35. How did Qing Qing communicate with her father?

    (A) Via email

    (B) Through texting

    (C) By phone call

36. What does Qing Qing's father need?

    (A) Fireworks

    (B) Spring couplets

    (C) Red pockets

Questions 37-38

親愛的媽媽：

　　對不起！我把今天要交的作業忘在家裡了。就是我畫的那張「白日依山盡，黃河入海流」的圖畫。我放在書桌上了，如果您方便的話，能請您送來學校給我嗎？

多謝！多謝！

青青　敬上

Questions 37-38

亲爱的妈妈：

　　对不起！我把今天要交的作业忘在家里了。就是我画的那张"白日依山尽，黄河入海流"的图画。我放在书桌上了，如果您方便的话，能请您送来学校给我吗？

多谢！多谢！

青青　敬上

37. Which item did Qing Qing leave at home?

    (A) A drawing

    (B) A textbook

    (C) A notebook

38. According to the note, what time of the day does the verse line describe?

    (A) Noon

    (B) Morning

    (C) Evening

II. AP Practice
1. Writing (E-mail Response)

Question 1 of 2: Read this e-mail from a friend and then type a response.

發件人:小華

郵件主題:你喜歡哪首詩

　　我們這星期學了《静夜詩》和《尋隱者不遇》這兩首唐詩,你喜歡哪一首?爲什麽?

发件人: 小华

邮件主题: 你喜欢哪首诗

　　我们这星期学了《静夜诗》和《寻隐者不遇》这两首唐诗,你喜欢哪一首? 为什么?

2. Writing (Story Narration)

Question 2 of 2: The four pictures below present a story. Imagine you are writing this story to a friend. Narrate the complete story as shown in the pictures. Give your story a beginning, a middle, and an end. Please write the story on a separate sheet of paper or type it down on a computer.

III. Idioms/Frequently Used Phrases (Traditional)

You can listen to idioms, phrases, and questions on your CD.

平易近人	píng yì jìn rén	approachable; easy to get along with
小巧玲瓏	xiǎo qiǎo líng lóng	small and cute
夜深人靜	yè shēn rén jìng	deep into the night
琅琅上口	láng láng shàng kǒu	to recite quite fluently
才華洋溢	cái huá yáng yì	talented

1. 李白是唐朝有名的詩人，他的詩很美，並且＿＿＿＿＿＿＿，一般人都看得懂。

2. 有一年秋天，李白離家在外，＿＿＿＿＿＿＿時，他寫下了著名的靜夜思。

3. 李白的靜夜思，讀起來＿＿＿＿＿＿＿，許多孩子都會背誦。

4. 李白是一位＿＿＿＿＿＿＿的詩人，他的詩渾然天成。

5. 青青也會作詩，爸爸給的獎品是一部＿＿＿＿＿＿＿的手機。

III.   Idioms/Frequently Used Phrases (Simplified)

You can listen to idioms, phrases, and questions on your CD.

平易近人	píng yì jìn rén	approachable; easy to get along with
小巧玲珑	xiǎo qiǎo líng lóng	small and cute
夜深人静	yè shēn rén jìng	deep into the night
琅琅上口	láng láng shàng kǒu	to recite quite fluently
才华洋溢	cái huá yáng yì	talented

1. 李白是唐朝有名的诗人，他的诗很美，并且_____，一般人都看得懂。

2. 有一年秋天，李白离家在外，_____时，他写下了著名的静夜思。

3. 李白的静夜思，读起来_____，许多孩子都会背诵。

4. 李白是一位_____的诗人，他的诗浑然天成。

5. 青青也会作诗，爸爸给的奖品是一部_____的手机。

IV. Vocabulary/Phrase Review

Please translate the following words/phrases into Chinese.

Lesson 4: (based on the text book p.127)

English	Chinese	English	Chinese
classroom		very deep	
classical poetry		very difficult	
frosted		to know (a person)	
to recite		question; problem; issue	
to see (something far away)			
to lower one's head			
homeland; home village			
prize; award, trophy			
picture; painting			
pine tree			
to pick herbs			

課文：送什麼禮物　　　　　　　課文：送什么礼物
故事：蔡倫造紙的故事　　　　　故事：蔡伦造纸的故事

I. SAT Practice: 1. Listening (10) 2. Usage (18) 3. Reading Comprehension (10)

II. AP Practice: 1. Writing (E-mail Response) 2. Writing (Story Narration)

III. Idioms/Frequently Used Phrases

IV. Vocabulary/Phrase Review

I. SAT Practice
SECTION I LISTENING   Approximate time – 10 minutes

PART A
Directions: In this part of the test, you will hear some short questions, statements, or commands, as well as responses, in Mandarin Chinese. Each question, statement, or command is followed by three responses, designated by letters (A), (B), and (C). You will hear the recording only one time. You will only hear, but not see, the recording materials. Therefore, you must listen very attentively. Select the best response and circle the answer.
Now listen to the recording.

Circle the answer.

Questions 1-4

1.　(A)　(B)　(C)

2.　(A)　(B)　(C)

3.　(A)　(B)　(C)

4.　(A)　(B)　(C)

PART B
Directions: You will now hear a series of short conversations. After each conversation, you will answer one or more questions about it. You will hear the conversations only once. You will only hear, but not see, the conversation materials. Therefore, you must listen very attentively. Select and circle your answer choice to each question. You will have fifteen seconds to answer each question.
Now listen to the first conversation.

Questions 5-6

5.　According to the conversation, what can they buy in the store?

(A) Business cards

(B) Laptops

(C) Photo albums

6.　Which of the following items is NOT sold in the store?

(A) Birthday cards

(B) Books

(C) Snacks

Questions 7-8

7. What is this conversation mainly about?

    (A) The advantages of a gift card.

    (B) The wedding gifts that the bride received.

    (C) A shopping list for the wedding.

8. What did Lily buy?

    (A) Dishes, sheets, pots

    (B) Table clothes, towels, flowers,

    (C) Vases, dishes, pots

Questions 9-10

9. Who made the birthday card?

    (A) Ming-Ming's friend

    (B) Ming-Ming

    (C) The boy

10. What items were used to make the birthday card?

    (A) Old fabric, dyes, dry flowers

    (B) Old fabric, leaves ,recycled paper

    (C) recycled paper, markers, old fabric

SECTION II   USAGE
Suggested time – 20 minutes/Questions 11-28

Directions: This section consists of a number of incomplete sentences. Each sentence has three answer choices. Select one word or phrase to fill in the blank to make the sentence complete both structurally and logically.

The questions are presented in four different ways: traditional characters, simplified characters, pinyin romanization and the Chinese phonetic alphabet (bopomofo). Zhuyin and pinyin of each question are posted on the Meizhou Chinese website. You can also listen to the questions on your CD.

11. 有一句名言:機會是留___準備好
    的人。

    (A) 要
    (B) 在
    (C) 給

12. 我自己做了一____畫冊。

    (A) 本
    (B) 個
    (C) 張

13. 你是____做禮券的？

    (A) 這麼
    (B) 這樣
    (C) 怎麼

14. 要____上課，不要遲到。

    (A) 有時
    (B) 準時
    (C) 總是

15. 這台電腦是我的，___都是別人的。
    (A) 其它
    (B) 其中
    (C) 其實

16. 古時候的人___字寫在竹片上。
    (A) 把
    (B) 給
    (C) 拿

11. 有一句名言: 机会是留___准备好
    的人。

    (A) 要
    (B) 在
    (C) 给

12. 我自己做了一____画册。

    (A) 本
    (B) 个
    (C) 张

13. 你是____做礼券的？

    (A) 这么
    (B) 这样
    (C) 怎么

14. 要____上课，不要迟到。

    (A) 有时
    (B) 准时
    (C) 总是

15. 这台电脑是我的，___都是别人的。
    (A) 其它
    (B) 其中
    (C) 其实

16. 古时候的人___字写在竹片上。
    (A) 把
    (B) 给
    (C) 拿

17. 我每天坐校車上學很_____。
    (A) 順利
    (B) 方便
    (C) 順便

17. 我每天坐校车上学很_____。
    (A) 顺利
    (B) 方便
    (C) 顺便

18. 他買了一____新車。
    (A) 座
    (B) 輛
    (C) 個

18. 他买了一____新车。
    (A) 座
    (B) 辆
    (C) 个

19. 我要先去圖書館，___才回家。
    (A) 然後
    (B) 以後
    (C) 後來

19. 我要先去图书馆，___才回家。
    (A) 然后
    (B) 以后
    (C) 后来

20. 互聯網的發明使新聞傳播得____快。
    (A) 更
    (B) 還
    (C) 再

20. 互联网的发明使新闻传播得____快。
    (A) 更
    (B) 还
    (C) 再

21. 我每天上學，都____這家糕餅店。
    (A) 已經
    (B) 經過
    (C) 經常

21. 我每天上学，都____这家糕饼店。
    (A) 已经
    (B) 经过
    (C) 经常

22. 這瓶藥的有效期限____哪天?
    (A) 有
    (B) 要
    (C) 是

22. 这瓶药的有效期限____哪天?
    (A) 有
    (B) 要
    (C) 是

23. 電腦__可以用來寫作業，___可以
    玩遊戲。
    (A) 不過…還
    (B) 如果…還
    (C) 不但…還

24. 媽媽____許多蔬菜放進鍋子裡，煮了
    一大鍋湯。
    (A) 讓
    (B) 給
    (C) 把

25. 現在_____的人喜歡上網買東西。
    (A) 越來越大
    (B) 越來越多
    (C) 越來越長

26. 他生病了，___心情很不好。
    (A) 因為
    (B) 因此
    (C) 應該

27. 我們要多運動，才不會___長___胖。
    (A) 更…更
    (B) 快…快
    (C) 越…越

28. 我們_____。
    (A) 要懂得如何廢物利用
    (B) 如何要懂得廢物利用
    (C) 廢物利用要如何懂得

23. 电脑__可以用来写作业，___可以
    玩游戏。
    (A) 不过…还
    (B) 如果…还
    (C) 不但…还

24. 妈妈____许多蔬菜放进锅子里，煮了
    一大锅汤。
    (A) 让
    (B) 给
    (C) 把

25. 现在_____的人喜欢上网买东西。
    (A) 越来越大
    (B) 越来越多
    (C) 越来越长

26. 他生病了，___心情很不好。
    (A) 因为
    (B) 因此
    (C) 应该

27. 我们要多运动，才不会___长___胖。
    (A) 更…更
    (B) 快…快
    (C) 越…越

28. 我们_____。
    (A) 要懂得如何废物利用
    (B) 如何要懂得废物利用
    (C) 废物利用要如何懂得

Directions: Read the following texts carefully. Each is followed by one or more questions or incomplete statements. Circle the best answer according to the text.

Questions 29-30

新華禮品店

$100 元   禮券

限在本店使用

不能兌換現金

有效期限：永不過期

Questions 29-30

新华礼品店

$100 元   礼券

限在本店使用

不能兑换现金

有效期限: 永不过期

29. Which item does the above information resemble?

(A) A coupon

(B) A gift certificate

(C) A business card

30. Which of the following statements about the item is INCORRECT?

(A) It can only be used at Xing Hua shop.

(B) It can be exchanged for cash.

(C) It has no expiration date.

Question 31

姐姐：

你不是要買一隻電動按摩器給媽媽嗎？你看這款怎麼樣？上網訂購又快又方便。

明明上

Question 31

姐姐:

你不是要买一只电动按摩器给妈妈吗？你看这款怎么样？上网订购又快又方便。

明明上

31. According to the text, which of the following statements is NOT true?

(A) Ming Ming will buy an electric massager for her mother.

(B) Ming Ming prefers to buy things online.

(C) Ming Ming suggested that her sister buy an electric massager online.

「送禮」不是一件簡單的事。人們常常花了許多錢和時間買的禮物，收禮物的人卻不喜歡。

如果買禮物卡當禮物就沒有這個問題了，因為買禮物卡省時省力，並且禮物卡就像現金一樣好用，收到禮物卡的人可以自己買喜歡的東西。

32. According to the text, why do many people NOT like to buy gifts?
   (A) The receivers may not like the gifts they are given.
   (B) The gifts are too expensive.
   (C) People do not like to spend money on gifts.

Questions 34-35

環保回收服務站

地點：華美老人中心停車場

時間：星期二到星期五

早上九點到下午五點

本站只收報紙等印刷物

所有回收物，請送到環保回收中心。

34. Where is the recycling center located?
   (A) Inside the senior center's building
   (B) In the senior center's parking lot
   (C) Inside city hall

"送礼"不是一件简单的事。人们常常花了许多钱和时间买的礼物，收礼物的人却不喜欢。

如果买礼物卡当礼物就没有这个问题了，因为买礼物卡省时省力，并且礼物卡就像现金一样好用，收到礼物卡的人可以自己买喜欢的东西。

33. Which of the following is NOT a benefit of giving gift cards to people?
   (A) Gift cards are as easy to use as cash.
   (B) People do not need to spend time on selecting gifts.
   (C) Gift cards are cheaper.

Questions 34-35

环保回收服务站

地点: 华美老人中心停车场

时间: 星期二到星期五

早上九点到下午五点

本站只收报纸等印刷物

所有回收物，请送到环保回收中心。

35. Which of the following statements is CORRECT?
   (A) The recycling center accepts all recyclable items.
   (B) The recycling center is open from Tuesday to Friday.
   (C) The recycling service station accepts newspapers and clothing.

王老師說，做手工造紙很容易，只有三個步驟：
1. 把平常收集的廢紙，乾燥花草等用水泡軟。
2. 放入果汁機加水攪爛。
3. 用一個過濾器濾掉多餘的水就成紙漿。
4. 把紙漿鋪平曬乾，就是手工紙了。

Question 36

王老师说，做手工造纸很容易，只有三个步骤：
1. 把平常收集的废纸，干燥花草等用水泡软。
2. 放入果汁机加水搅烂。
3. 用一个过滤器滤掉多余的水就成纸浆。
4. 把纸浆铺平晒干，就是手工纸了。

36. According to the instructions from Ms. Wang, which of the following steps is NOT mentioned?

(A) Adding water to the blender and mixing until completely blended

(B) Collecting recycled paper and dried flowers and putting them in water to soften them

(C) Spreading out the paper pulp and putting it in a jar

Questions 37-38

電腦和互聯網的發明改變了人類使用紙的習慣。現在的人很少用紙寫信，大多用電子郵件，還有許多人在網上交電費、水費、電話費等等，節省了許多紙張。但是在網上購物的人越來越多，郵寄貨品使用了更多的紙盒和紙箱。

Questions 37-38

电脑和互联网的发明改变了人类使用纸的习惯。现在的人很少用纸写信，大多用电子邮件，还有许多人在网上交电费、水费、电话费等等，节省了许多纸张。但是在网上购物的人越来越多，邮寄货品使用了更多的纸盒和纸箱。

37. What is the main idea of this text?

(A) The invention of computer and internet changed the way people use paper.

(B) Using recycled paper changed people's way of life.

(C) Shopping online is an easier process than ever before.

38. Which of the following statements is NOT true?

(A) More people shop online nowadays.

(B) People use fewer boxes for shipping nowadays.

(C) People pay bills online.

II.   AP Practice
1. Writing (E-mail Response)

Question 1 of 2: Read this e-mail from a friend and then type a response.

發件人：小華

郵件主題：送禮

　　我收集了許多裝牛奶的紙盒，我很想用這些紙盒來做些有用的東西。希望你給我一些寶貴的建議，謝謝！

发件人：小华

邮件主题：送礼

　　我收集了许多装牛奶的纸盒，我很想用这些纸盒来做些有用的东西。希望你给我一些宝贵的建议，谢谢！

2. Writing (Story Narration)

Question 2 of 2: The four pictures below present a story. Imagine you are writing this story to a friend. Narrate the complete story as shown in the pictures. Give your story a beginning, a middle, and an end. Please write the story on a separate sheet of paper or type it down on a computer.

III. Idioms/Frequently Used Phrases (Traditional)

You can listen to idioms, phrases, and questions on your CD.

不聲不響	bù shēng bù xiǎng	quietly
一舉兩得	yì jǔ liǎng dé	to kill two birds with one stone
廢物利用	fèi wù lì yòng	utilization of waste material
一日千里	yí rì qiān lǐ	to make huge progress
靈機一動	líng jī yí dòng	to have a sudden inspiration
林林總總	lín lín zǒng zǒng	numerous

1. 明明＿＿＿＿＿＿＿＿地爲父母準備好了聖誕禮物。

2. 明明上勞作課時，忽然＿＿＿＿＿＿＿＿，他要做禮卷送給爸媽當聖誕

   禮物。

3. 明明送給父母的禮物，不但省錢而且實用，真是＿＿＿＿＿＿＿＿。

4. 紙的發明幫助中國文明達到＿＿＿＿＿＿＿＿的發展。

5. 人們用紙製造了＿＿＿＿＿＿＿＿各式各樣的日常用品。

6. ＿＿＿＿＿＿＿＿和資源回收是愛護地球最有效的方法。

III. Idioms/Frequently Used Phrases (Simplified)

You can listen to idioms, phrases, and questions on your CD.

不声不响	bù shēng bù xiǎng	quietly
一举两得	yì jǔ liǎng dé	to kill two birds with one stone
废物利用	fèi wù lì yòng	utilization of waste material
一日千里	yí rì qiān lǐ	to make huge progress
灵机一动	líng jī yí dòng	to have a sudden inspiration
林林总总	lín lín zǒng zǒng	numerous

1. 明明_____地为父母准备好了圣诞礼物。

2. 明明上劳作课时，忽然_____，他要做礼卷送给爸妈当圣诞礼物。

3. 明明送给父母的礼物，不但省钱而且实用，真是_____。

4. 纸的发明帮助中国文明达到_____的发展。

5. 人们用纸制造了_____各式各样的日常用品。

6. _____和资源回收是爱护地球最有效的方法。

IV. Vocabulary/Phrase Review

Please translate the following words/phrases into Chinese.

Lesson 5: (based on the text book p.127-128)

English	Chinese	English	Chinese
gift		craftwork	
punctual; on time		rag	
to prepare; to arrange; to get ready		waste paper	
the first volume		valid period	
gift certificate		company	
super			
grade (class)			
making paper			
to help; to assist			
backache			
to fulfill the duty to a parent (filial duty)			

美洲華語第五冊第六課

課文：怎樣吃才健康

故事：食物金字塔

美洲华语第五册第六课

课文：怎样吃才健康

故事：食物金字塔

I.   SAT Practice: 1. Listening (10) 2. Usage (18) 3. Reading Comprehension (10)

II. AP Practice: 1. Writing (E-mail Response) 2. Writing (Story Narration)

III. Idioms/Frequently Used Phrases

IV. Vocabulary/Phrase Review

I.   SAT Practice
SECTION I   LISTENING   Approximate time – 10 minutes

PART A
Directions: In this part of the test, you will hear some short questions, statements, or commands, as well as responses, in Mandarin Chinese. Each question, statement, or command is followed by three responses, designated by letters (A), (B), and (C). You will hear the recording only one time. You will only hear, but not see, the recording materials. Therefore, you must listen very attentively. Select the best response and circle the answer.
Now listen to the recording.

Circle the answer.

Questions 1-4

1.   (A)   (B)   (C)

2.   (A)   (B)   (C)

3.   (A)   (B)   (C)

4.   (A)   (B)   (C)

PART B
Directions: You will now hear a series of short conversations. After each conversation, you will answer one or more questions about it. You will hear the conversations only once. You will only hear, but not see, the conversation materials. Therefore, you must listen very attentively. Select and circle your answer choice to each question. You will have fifteen seconds to answer each question.
Now listen to the first conversation.

Questions 5-6

5.   What kind of food is NOT mentioned in the conversation?
(A) Snacks
(B) Noodles
(C) Vegetables

6.   According to the conversation, which of the following statements is NOT true?
(A) The girl is preparing a dinner party this weekend.
(B) The girl is going to make beef noodle soup.
(C) Beef and noodles are on sale this week.

Question 7

7. What exercise does the boy do?
   - (A) He walks 30 minutes a day.
   - (B) He swims year round.
   - (C) He swims 30 minutes every day.

Question 8

8. Which of the following is NOT mentioned in the conversation?
   - (A) The ingredients
   - (B) The expiration dates
   - (C) The prices

Questions 9-10

9. Which of the following statements is true?
   - (A) The girl loves sweet snacks.
   - (B) The boy loves sweets.
   - (C) Both of them love soda.

10. Which of the following is NOT mentioned in the conversation?
    - (A) Fruit juice
    - (B) Diet cola
    - (C) Potato chips

SECTION II   USAGE
Suggested time – 20 minutes/Questions 11-28

Directions: This section consists of a number of incomplete sentences. Each sentence has three answer choices. Select one word or phrase to fill in the blank to make the sentence complete both structurally and logically.

The questions are presented in four different ways: traditional characters, simplified characters, pinyin romanization and the Chinese phonetic alphabet (bopomofo). Zhuyin and pinyin of each question are posted on the Meizhou Chinese website. You can also listen to the questions on your CD.

11. 我們___去買蔬菜，___去買肉。

(A) 是…還

(B) 要…再

(C) 先…再

12. _____上市的小白菜非常新鮮。

(A) 剛

(B) 就

(C) 來

13. 菠菜很便宜，買兩___回去吧。

(A) 個

(B) 把

(C) 條

14. ___! 你可以把這本書拿回去看。

(A) 沒話說

(B) 沒話講

(C) 沒問題

15. 她一個人在房間裡_____，不知道

在跟誰說話。

(A) 三言兩語

(B) 長話短說

(C) 自言自語

16. 媽媽買了兩___葡萄乾。

(A) 盒

(B) 個

(C) 把

11. 我们___去买蔬菜，___去买肉。

(A) 是…还

(B) 要…再

(C) 先…再

12. _____上市的小白菜非常新鲜。

(A) 刚

(B) 就

(C) 来

13. 菠菜很便宜，买两___回去吧。

(A) 个

(B) 把

(C) 条

14. ___! 你可以把这本书拿回去看。

(A) 没话说

(B) 没话讲

(C) 没问题

15. 她一个人在房间里_____，不知道

在跟谁说话。

(A) 三言两语

(B) 长话短说

(C) 自言自语

16. 妈妈买了两___葡萄干。

(A) 盒

(B) 个

(C) 把

17. 青青幫媽媽做許多家務事，她___媽媽
　　的好幫手。
　　(A) 可要
　　(B) 可是
　　(C) 可能

18. 他_____在開玩笑。
　　(A) 只是
　　(B) 只要
　　(C) 只有

19. 光吃得好還不夠，___要多運動。
　　(A) 才
　　(B) 就
　　(C) 還

20. 爸爸___媽媽寫的購物單，把東西都買
　　回來了。
　　(A) 照著
　　(B) 笑著
　　(C) 聽著

21. 多吃蔬菜__身體好。
　　(A) 對
　　(B) 給
　　(C) 是

22. 我們___少吃零食。
　　(A) 最後
　　(B) 最好
　　(C) 最初

17. 青青帮妈妈做许多家务事，她___妈妈
　　的好帮手。
　　(A) 可要
　　(B) 可是
　　(C) 可能

18. 他_____在开玩笑。
　　(A) 只是
　　(B) 只要
　　(C) 只有

19. 光吃得好还不够，___要多运动。
　　(A) 才
　　(B) 就
　　(C) 还

20. 爸爸___妈妈写的购物单，把东西都买
　　回来了。
　　(A) 照着
　　(B) 笑着
　　(C) 听着

21. 多吃蔬菜__身体好。
　　(A) 对
　　(B) 给
　　(C) 是

22. 我们___少吃零食。
　　(A) 最后
　　(B) 最好
　　(C) 最初

23. 開車的時候要___路上的行人。
    (A) 注重
    (B) 重視
    (C) 注意

24. 你覺得要___吃才健康？
    (A) 怎樣
    (B) 這樣
    (C) 這麼

25. 吃完飯_____，我陪爺爺去散步。
    (A) 後面
    (B) 以後
    (C) 後來

26. 牛油和豬油___是動物油。
    (A) 只
    (B) 還
    (C) 都

27. 家裡的錢___媽媽管。
    (A) 把
    (B) 由
    (C) 來

28. 媽媽說_____。
    (A) 對身體好多吃蔬菜
    (B) 多吃蔬菜對身體好
    (C) 對身體好蔬菜多吃

23. 开车的时候要___路上的行人。
    (A) 注重
    (B) 重视
    (C) 注意

24. 你觉得要___吃才健康？
    (A) 怎样
    (B) 这样
    (C) 这么

25. 吃完饭_____，我陪爷爷去散步。
    (A) 后面
    (B) 以后
    (C) 后来

26. 牛油和猪油___是动物油。
    (A) 只
    (B) 还
    (C) 都

27. 家里的钱___妈妈管。
    (A) 把
    (B) 由
    (C) 来

28. 妈妈说_____。
    (A) 对身体好多吃蔬菜
    (B) 多吃蔬菜对身体好
    (C) 对身体好蔬菜多吃

Directions: Read the following texts carefully. Each is followed by one or more questions or incomplete statements. Circle the best answer according to the text.

Questions 29-30

園林市農夫市場

每星期日早上九點到十二點
新鮮水果蔬菜、麵包、鮮花、
堅果、珍奇果樹
地點：園林大學停車場
可免費停車

Questions 29-30

园林市农夫市场

每星期日早上九点到十二点
新鲜水果蔬菜、面包、鲜花、
坚果、珍奇果树
地点: 园林大学停车场
可免费停车

29. What will you find in this market?

(A) Bread, cakes and fast food

(B) Bread, flowers, art and crafts

(C) Vegetables, fruits and fruit trees

30. Which of the following statements is CORRECT?

(A) Parking is free for customers.

(B) The market is open every day.

(C) The market also sells fast food.

Questions 31-32

為了慶祝中國新年，王老師用糯米做了幾個紅棗年糕、紅豆年糕和花生年糕帶來請大家吃。王老師說：「年糕」和「年高」的發音相同。過年吃年糕，祝福你們年年長高，年年進步。

Questions 31-32

为了庆祝中国新年，王老师用糯米做了几个红枣年糕、红豆年糕和花生年糕带来请大家吃。王老师说: "年糕"和"年高"的发音相同。过年吃年糕，祝福你们年年长高，年年进步。

31. What did Miss Wang use to make her Chinese New Year Cake?

    (A) Green beans, red beans, and peanuts

    (B) Raisins, red beans and peanuts

    (C) Dates, red beans and peanuts

32. The pronunciation of Niangao sounds like "year high", which symbolizes _____.

    (A) A higher living cost

    (B) Greater progress in the new year

    (C) A higher living standard

Questions 33-34

> 哥哥：
>
> 　今天是爸爸的生日，媽媽做了牛肉麵和許多菜，有爸爸愛吃的紅燒魚，也有我們愛吃的甜酸肉。六點鐘開飯。媽媽說放學後要你坐校車回來，她就不去接你了。
>
> 　　　　　　　　　　中中上

Questions 33-34

> 哥哥:
>
> 　今天是爸爸的生日，妈妈做了牛肉面和许多菜，有爸爸爱吃的红烧鱼，也有我们爱吃的甜酸肉。六点钟开饭。妈妈说放学后要你坐校车回来，她就不去接你了。
>
> 　　　　　　　　　　中中上

33. Which of the following statements is INCORRECT?

    (A) This is a big surprise birthday party.

    (B) Zhong Zhong's brother will take the school bus home.

    (C) The dinner will start at six o'clock.

34. Which of the following is Zhong Zhong's favorite dish?

    (A) Fish in soy bean sauce

    (B) Sweet and sour pork

    (C) Beef noodle soup

Questions 35-36

> 　今天是臘八節，明明跟媽媽一起做臘八粥。媽媽說做臘八粥要先煮白米、小米、紅米、紅豆、黑豆、花生和紅棗，一個小時後再加入葡萄乾和冰糖就完成了。

Questions 35-36

> 　今天是腊八节，明明跟妈妈一起做腊八粥。妈妈说做腊八粥要先煮白米、小米、红米、红豆、黑豆、花生和红枣，一个小时后再加入葡萄干和冰糖就完成了。

35. Which of the following ingredients is NOT in the recipe for La Ba Porridge?

(A) Peanuts

(B) Green beans

(C) Dates

36. Which of the following statements is INCORRECT?

(A) This porridge includes 3 kinds of rice and 3 kinds of beans.

(B) It takes one hour to cook La Ba porridge.

(C) The last step is adding raisins and sugar cubes.

Questions 37-38

早餐、午餐、晚餐，怎樣吃才健康？

下面是營養專家的建議：

1. 早上吃得好，中午吃得飽，晚上吃得少。
2. 每頓飯營養要均衡，要有蔬菜、水果、牛奶、魚肉、蛋或豆類以及五穀類。
3. 盡量吃少糖、少鹽、少油，沒有味精的食物。

Questions 37-38

早餐、午餐、晚餐，怎样吃才健康？

下面是营养专家的建议：

1. 早上吃得好，中午吃得饱，晚上吃得少。
2. 每顿饭营养要均衡，要有蔬菜、水果、牛奶、鱼肉、蛋或豆类以及五谷类。
3. 尽量吃少糖、少盐、少油，没有味精的食物。

37. What is the main idea of this text?

(A) Eating healthy food is important.

(B) Dieting is not easy.

(C) Vitamins are nutritious.

38. Which one of the following advice is NOT mentioned in the text?

(A) Eat more for breakfast and eat less for dinner.

(B) Eat less oil and avoid MSG.

(C) Regular exercise is important.

II. AP Practice
1. Writing (E-mail Response)

Question 1 of 2: Read this e-mail from a friend and then type a response.

發件人:小華
郵件主題:食物金字塔

　　食物金字塔把食物分成六類，請你告訴我哪一類我們應該吃得最少？媽媽說我們不能吃太多的零食。爲什麼不能呢？

发件人: 小华
邮件主题: 食物金字塔

　　食物金字塔把食物分成六类，请你告诉我哪一类我们应该吃得最少？妈妈说我们不能吃太多的零食。为什么不能呢？

2. Writing (Story Narration)

Question 2 of 2: The four pictures below present a story. Imagine you are writing this story to a friend. Narrate the complete story as shown in the pictures. Give your story a beginning, a middle, and an end. Please write the story on a separate sheet of paper or type it down on a computer.

III. Idioms/Frequently Used Phrases (Traditional)

You can listen to idioms, phrases, and questions on your CD.

分ㄈㄣ門ㄇㄣˊ別ㄅㄧㄝˊ類ㄌㄟˋ	fēn mén bié lèi	categories
詳ㄒㄧㄤˊ詳ㄒㄧㄤˊ細ㄒㄧˋ細ㄒㄧˋ	xiáng xiáng xì xì	detailed
美ㄇㄟˇ味ㄨㄟˋ可ㄎㄜˇ口ㄎㄡˇ	měi wèi kě kǒu	delicious
井ㄐㄧㄥˇ井ㄐㄧㄥˇ有ㄧㄡˇ條ㄊㄧㄠˊ	jǐng jǐng yǒu tiáo	in perfect order
老ㄌㄠˇ老ㄌㄠˇ實ㄕˊ實ㄕˊ	lǎo lǎo shí shí	honestly
大ㄉㄚˋ魚ㄩˊ大ㄉㄚˋ肉ㄖㄡˋ	dà yú dà ròu	a feast; abundant fish and meat

1. 超級市場賣的東西很多，但是都＿＿＿＿＿＿＿＿地放在不同的區域，

   讓顧客找起來方便。

2. 各種零食也都＿＿＿＿＿＿＿＿，整整齊齊地擺在架子上。

3. 老師上課時＿＿＿＿＿＿＿＿地解説了食物金字塔的重要性。

4. 餐廳的菜雖然＿＿＿＿＿＿＿＿，可是不一定健康。

5. 如果我們＿＿＿＿＿＿＿＿照著食物金字塔的飲食比例吃東西，身體才

   會健康。

6. 要吃得健康，不能只是吃＿＿＿＿＿＿＿＿，而是要多吃蔬菜。

III. Idioms/Frequently Used Phrases (Simplified)

You can listen to idioms, phrases, and questions on your CD.

分门别类	fēn mén bié lèi	categories
详详细细	xiáng xiáng xì xì	detailed
美味可口	měi wèi kě kǒu	delicious
井井有条	jǐng jǐng yǒu tiáo	in perfect order
老老实实	lǎo lǎo shí shí	honestly
大鱼大肉	dà yú dà ròu	a feast; abundant fish and meat

1. 超级市场卖的东西很多，但是都_____地放在不同的区域，让顾客找起来方便。

2. 各种零食也都_____，整整齐齐地摆在架子上。

3. 老师上课时_____地解说了食物金字塔的重要性。

4. 餐厅的菜虽然_____，可是不一定健康。

5. 如果我们_____照着食物金字塔的饮食比例吃东西，身体才会健康。

6. 要吃得健康，不能只是吃_____，而是要多吃蔬菜。

IV. Vocabulary/Phrase Review

Please translate the following words/phrases into Chinese.

Lesson 6: (based on the text book p.128)

English	Chinese	English	Chinese
snack bar		to pay (with money)	
to accompany; to go with		cart	
body		gym	
just came out into the market		health	
fruit category		to manage; to administer: to direct	
bean curd in red sauce			
fried rice			
spare rib soup			
snacks			
raisin			
bread			

I. SAT Practice: 1. Listening (10) 2. Usage (18) 3. Reading Comprehension (10)

II. AP Practice: 1. Writing (E-mail Response) 2. Writing (Story Narration)

III. Idioms/Frequently Used Phrases

IV. Vocabulary/Phrase Review

I. SAT Practice
SECTION I   LISTENING   Approximate time – 10 minutes

PART A

Directions: In this part of the test, you will hear some short questions, statements, or commands, as well as responses, in Mandarin Chinese. Each question, statement, or command is followed by three responses, designated by letters (A), (B), and (C). You will hear the recording only one time. You will only hear, but not see, the recording materials. Therefore, you must listen very attentively. Select the best response and circle the answer.
Now listen to the recording.

Circle the answer.

Questions 1-4

1. (A)   (B)   (C)

2. (A)   (B)   (C)

3. (A)   (B)   (C)

4. (A)   (B)   (C)

PART B

Directions: You will now hear a series of short conversations. After each conversation, you will answer one or more questions about it. You will hear the conversations only once. You will only hear, but not see, the conversation materials. Therefore, you must listen very attentively. Select and circle your answer choice to each question. You will have fifteen seconds to answer each question.
Now listen to the first conversation.

Question 5

5. Which of the following statements is true?
    (A) The boy didn't want to leave home so soon.
    (B) The boy has to study abroad soon.
    (C) The boy's brother went to France to attend college.

Question 6

6. What is the girl's favorite sport?
    (A) Volleyball
    (B) Soccer
    (C) American football

Question 7

7. How did the boy get the tickets?
    (A) He bought them online.
    (B) He bought them at the venue.
    (C) He was not able to get any tickets.

Question 8

8. Which of the following is the reason
    The Suns won the championship this
    year?
    (A) They are good at shooting.
    (B) They are good at passing.
    (C) They have a good defense.

Question 9

9. Why are the Principal and the Mayor
    praising the boy?
    (A) He donated his allowance to poor
         and sick children.
    (B) He won the first place in math
         contest.
    (C) He saved the most money in
         school.

Question 10

10. Which of the following is NOT a
     benefit of joining a sports camp ?
     (A) Making new friends
     (B) Learning different sports
     (C) Exercising everyday

SECTION II   USAGE
Suggested time – 20 minutes/Questions 11-28

Directions: This section consists of a number of incomplete sentences. Each sentence has three answer choices. Select one word or phrase to fill in the blank to make the sentence complete both structurally and logically.

The questions are presented in four different ways: traditional characters, simplified characters, pinyin romanization and the Chinese phonetic alphabet (bopomofo). Zhuyin and pinyin of each question are posted on the Meizhou Chinese website. You can also listen to the questions on your CD.

11. 昨天表哥___我說，他又交了一個
　　女朋友。

　　(A) 跟
　　(B) 來
　　(C) 為

12. 讀書的最大好處____增進知識。
　　(A) 就有
　　(B) 就是
　　(C) 就好

13. 我參加足球隊___，___慢慢地愛上這項
　　運動。

　　(A) 然後…才
　　(B) 後來…就
　　(C) 以後…才

14. 我____和表哥一起上電腦課。
　　(A) 決心
　　(B) 決定
　　(C) 絕對

15. 昨天數學課有小考，____今天又
　　要考？
　　(A) 怎麼
　　(B) 這麼
　　(C) 什麼

16. 這一大盤餃子，____一個裡面有
　　硬幣。
　　(A) 其實
　　(B) 其它
　　(C) 其中

11. 昨天表哥___我说，他又交了一个
　　女朋友。

　　(A) 跟
　　(B) 来
　　(C) 为

12. 读书的最大好处____增进知识。
　　(A) 就有
　　(B) 就是
　　(C) 就好

13. 我参加足球队___，___慢慢地爱上这项
　　运动。

　　(A) 然后…才
　　(B) 后来…就
　　(C) 以后…才

14. 我____和表哥一起上电脑课。
　　(A) 决心
　　(B) 决定
　　(C) 绝对

15. 昨天数学课有小考，____今天又
　　要考？
　　(A) 怎么
　　(B) 这么
　　(C) 什么

16. 这一大盘饺子，____一个里面有
　　硬币。
　　(A) 其实
　　(B) 其它
　　(C) 其中

17. 我們___在一起打籃球。
    (A) 常常
    (B) 長久
    (C) 然後

18. 我____把房間整理乾淨，___幫媽媽
    洗碗。
    (A) 雖然…可是
    (B) 先…然後
    (C) 因為…所以

19. 小留學生___想家，____夜裡常常
    哭醒。
    (A) 如果…就
    (B) 因為…所以
    (C) 可是…卻

20. 他才來_____，就交了許多朋友。
    (A) 不久
    (B) 長久
    (C) 久了

21. 不同民族的學生在這個學校_____，
    和平相處。
    (A) 四面八方
    (B) 七上八下
    (C) 打成一片

22. 明天我們學校有一____足球賽。
    (A) 場
    (B) 個
    (C) 部

17. 我们___在一起打篮球。
    (A) 常常
    (B) 长久
    (C) 然后

18. 我____把房间整理干净，___帮妈妈
    洗碗。
    (A) 虽然…可是
    (B) 先…然后
    (C) 因为…所以

19. 小留学生___想家，____夜里常常
    哭醒。
    (A) 如果…就
    (B) 因为…所以
    (C) 可是…却

20. 他才来_____，就交了许多朋友。
    (A) 不久
    (B) 长久
    (C) 久了

21. 不同民族的学生在这个学校_____，
    和平相处。
    (A) 四面八方
    (B) 七上八下
    (C) 打成一片

22. 明天我们学校有一____足球赛。
    (A) 场
    (B) 个
    (C) 部

23. 熟睡的小弟弟，＿＿＿醒了。
   (A) 然後
   (B) 果然
   (C) 忽然

24. 每天上學＿＿＿，他都會檢查書包裡面的
   東西。
   (A) 之後
   (B) 前面
   (C) 之前

25. 我有許多件大衣，＿＿＿這件是紅色的。
   (A) 只能
   (B) 只有
   (C) 只要

26. 那個女孩＿＿＿長得很甜美，＿＿＿很
   聰明。
   (A) 就算…可是
   (B) 就是…而且
   (C) 不但…而且

27. 這場球賽＿＿＿是誰贏了？
   (A) 果然
   (B) 結果
   (C) 以後

28. 今天下午，＿＿＿＿＿＿＿＿＿＿。
   (A) 王老師分別見了我們三個同學
   (B) 王老師見了分別我們三個同學
   (C) 王老師見了我們分別三個同學

23. 熟睡的小弟弟，＿＿＿醒了。
   (A) 然后
   (B) 果然
   (C) 忽然

24. 每天上學＿＿＿，他都会检查书包里面的
   东西。
   (A) 之后
   (B) 前面
   (C) 之前

25. 我有许多件大衣，＿＿＿这件是红色的。
   (A) 只能
   (B) 只有
   (C) 只要

26. 那个女孩＿＿＿长得很甜美，＿＿＿很
   聪明。
   (A) 就算…可是
   (B) 就是…而且
   (C) 不但…而且

27. 这场球赛＿＿＿是谁赢了？
   (A) 果然
   (B) 结果
   (C) 以后

28. 今天下午，＿＿＿＿＿＿＿＿＿＿。
   (A) 王老师分别见了我们三个同学
   (B) 王老师见了分别我们三个同学
   (C) 王老师见了我们分别三个同学

SECTION III   READING COMPREHENSION
Suggested time – 20 minutes/ Questions 29 – 38

Directions: Read the following texts carefully. Each is followed by one or more questions or incomplete statements. Circle the best answer according to the text.

Question 29

> 清理中
> 請勿進入

Question 29

> 清理中
> 请勿进入

29. Where are you most likely to see this sign ?

   (A) Inside a gym
   (B) At the exit door of a swimming pool
   (C) At the entrance of a restroom

Questions 30-31

> 園林市飛魚游泳隊
> 暑期表演
> 上網註冊，免費參觀。
> www.flyingfishswim.com
> 咨詢電話：714-921-4751

Questions 30-31

> 园林市飞鱼游泳队
> 暑期表演
> 上网注册，免费参观。
> www.flyingfishswim.com
> 咨询电话： 714-921-4751

30. Which event is this advertisement promoting?

   (A) A trip to see flying fish
   (B) A swimming show
   (C) A swimming class registration

31. According to the advertisement, how can one participate?

   (A) By making a phone call
   (B) By buying tickets online
   (C) By registering online

Questions 32-33

Questions 32-33

園林小學　　室內運動場
每天開放 早上八點到晚上八點
使用規則：
1. 不准帶食物入內。
2. 請穿著運動服裝和運動鞋。
3. 運動器械使用後，請放回原位。
4. 只限本校學生使用。

園林小学　　室内运动场
每天开放 早上八点到晚上八点
使用规则：
1. 不准带食物入内。
2. 请穿着运动服装和运动鞋。
3. 运动器械使用后，请放回原位。
4. 只限本校学生使用。

32. What does this sign say?

(A) The rules of the school gym

(B) The rules of the school swimming pool

(C) The rules of the school soccer field

33. According to the rules on the sign, which of the following statements is INCORRECT?

(A) No food is allowed in the facility.

(B) One should always wear sneakers inside the facility.

(C) The facility is open to the school staff and students only.

Questions 34-35

Questions 34-35

園林市日報
[本報 20 日訊]
　十月十九日本市舉行加州小學組棒球決賽，園林小學迎戰新華小學。園林隊員發揮了團隊精神，打出三個滿壘的全壘打，戰勝了新華小學取得決賽第一名。

园林市日报
[本报 20 日讯]
　十月十九日本市举行加州小学组棒球决赛，园林小学迎战新华小学。园林队员发挥了团队精神，打出三个满垒的全垒打，战胜了新华小学取得决赛第一名。

34. What is this news report about?
(A) A baseball championship.
(B) A baseball preliminary.
(C) A baseball game.

35. Which of the following statements is true?
    (A) Xin-Hua Baseball Team hit three home runs.
    (B) Yuan-Lin Baseball Team hit three home runs.
    (C) Xin-Hua Baseball Team won the first place.

Questions 36-38

親愛的外公、外婆：

　　我有一個好消息！哥哥學校的紅帽隊大勝青葉隊取得冠軍。哥哥是投手，全家都去為他加油。球賽結束後，我們參加了慶功會才回家。

敬祝

　　　安康

　　　　　　中中　敬上

Questions 36-38

亲爱的外公、外婆：

　　我有一个好消息！哥哥学校的红帽队大胜青叶队取得冠军。哥哥是投手，全家都去为他加油。球赛结束后，我们参加了庆功会才回家。

敬祝

　　　安康

　　　　　　中中　敬上

36. To whom is this letter addressed to?
    (A) Zhong Zhong's grandparents on his mother's side.
    (B) Zhong Zhong's grandparents on his father's side.
    (C) Zhong Zhong's great grandparents on his father's side.

37. Which team is the winner?
    (A) Yuan Lin
    (B) Red Hats
    (C) Green Leaves

38. Which of the following statements is true?
    (A) Zhong Zhong's brother's team won a game.
    (B) Zhong Zhong played an important role in the game.
    (C) After the game, Zhong Zhong went home.

- 87 -

II. AP Practice
1. Writing (E-mail Response)

Question 1 of 2: Read this e-mail from a friend and then type a response.

發件人:青青
郵件主題:小留學生

　　小華是我的同學,今年暑假,小華的父母要把她送去台北念書,住在姑姑家。小華很內向,不會交朋友,她的中文也不好,所以她非常擔心,你有什麼建議嗎?

发件人: 青青
邮件主题: 小留学生

　　小华是我的同学,今年暑假,小华的父母要把她送去台北念书,住在姑姑家。小华很内向,不会交朋友,她的中文也不好,所以她非常担心,你有什么建议吗?

2. Writing (Story Narration)

Question 2 of 2: The four pictures below present a story. Imagine you are writing this story to a friend. Narrate the complete story as shown in the pictures. Give your story a beginning, a middle, and an end. Please write the story on a separate sheet of paper or type it down on a computer.

III. Idioms/Frequently Used Phrases (Traditional)

You can listen to idioms, phrases, and questions on your CD.

身強體健	shēn qiáng tǐ jiàn	strong and healthy
熱熱鬧鬧	rè rè nào nào	bustling with noise and excitement; lively
打成一片	dǎ chéng yí piàn	to become integrated with; to go with the crowd
飄洋過海	piāo yáng guò hǎi	to cross the seas
情同手足	qíng tóng shǒu zú	to be close like brothers; loving one another as brothers
落花流水	luò huā liú shuǐ	to be utterly defeated

1. 李教練在家裡開了一個＿＿＿＿＿＿＿＿的迎新會。

2. 1872 年，中國第一批小留學生，＿＿＿＿＿＿＿＿來到美國求學。

3. 小留學生們背井離鄉，生活在一起，最後成了＿＿＿＿＿＿＿＿的好朋友。

4. 小留學生們入鄉隨俗，很快就和當地的同學＿＿＿＿＿＿＿＿。

5. 小留學生們個個品學兼優，＿＿＿＿＿＿＿＿，他們還成立了一支棒球隊。

6. 回國之前，他們把 Oakland 棒球隊打得＿＿＿＿＿＿＿＿，贏得了那場球賽。

III. Idioms/Frequently Used Phrases (Simplified)

You can listen to idioms, phrases, and questions on your CD.

身强体健	shēn qiáng tǐ jiàn	strong and healthy
热热闹闹	rè rè nào nào	bustling with noise and excitement; lively
打成一片	dǎ chéng yí piàn	to become integrated with; to go with the crowd
飘洋过海	piāo yáng guò hǎi	to cross the seas
情同手足	qíng tóng shǒu zú	to be close like brothers; loving one another as brothers
落花流水	luò huā liú shuǐ	to be utterly defeated

1. 李教练在家里开了一个_____的迎新会。

2. 1872 年，中国第一批小留学生，_____来到美国求学。

3. 小留学生们背井离乡，生活在一起，最后成了_____的
   好朋友。

4. 小留学生们入乡随俗，很快就和当地的同学_____。

5. 小留学生们个个品学兼优，_____，他们还成立了一支
   棒球队。

6. 回国之前，他们把 Oakland 棒球队打得_____，赢得了
   那场球赛。

IV. Vocabulary/Phrase Review

Please translate the following words/phrases into Chinese.

Lesson 7: (based on the text book p.129)

English	Chinese	English	Chinese
to hold (an event)		a ball team	
short term		tennis	
sports camp		baseball	
to welcome		to decide; a decision	
to participate; to take part in		to pay close attention; to focus	
politics			
government			
coach			
to throw a ball			
to pass a ball			
to catch a ball			

美洲華語第五冊第八課
課文:誰是美國花木蘭
故事:花木蘭的故事

美洲华语第五册第八课
课文: 谁是美国花木兰
故事: 花木兰的故事

I. SAT Practice: 1. Listening (10) 2. Usage (18) 3. Reading Comprehension (10)

II. AP Practice: 1. Writing (E-mail Response) 2. Writing (Story Narration)

III. Idioms/Frequently Used Phrases

IV. Vocabulary/Phrase Review

I. SAT Practice
SECTION I   LISTENING   Approximate time – 10 minutes

PART A

Directions: In this part of the test, you will hear some short questions, statements, or commands, as well as responses, in Mandarin Chinese. Each question, statement, or command is followed by three responses, designated by letters (A), (B), and (C). You will hear the recording only one time. You will only hear, but not see, the recording materials. Therefore, you must listen very attentively. Select the best response and circle the answer.
Now listen to the recording.

Circle the answer.

Questions 1-4

1. (A)   (B)   (C)

2. (A)   (B)   (C)

3. (A)   (B)   (C)

4. (A)   (B)   (C)

PART B

Directions: You will now hear a series of short conversations. After each conversation, you will answer one or more questions about it. You will hear the conversations only once. You will only hear, but not see, the conversation materials. Therefore, you must listen very attentively. Select and circle your answer choice to each question. You will have fifteen seconds to answer each question.
Now listen to the first conversation.

Questions 5-6

5.   Which of the military services is NOT mentioned in this conversation?

(A) Navy

(B) Air Force

(C) Army

6.   Which of the following statements is true?

(A) The girl wants to join the Air Force.

(B) The boy gets seasick, so he is going to join the Army.

(C) The girl's brother is a naval officer.

Questions 7-8

7. What is the conversation about?

   (A) U.S. National holidays

   (B) Worldwide Veterans Day

   (C) U.S. Veterans Day

8. Which of the following statements is NOT true?

   (A) Veterans Day is a not a national holiday.

   (B) Most schools in the U.S. are closed on Veterans Day.

   (C) World War I ended on Nov.11th.

Questions 9-10

9. Where did this conversation most likely take place?

   (A) In front of a Chinese bookstore.

   (B) In front of a Chinese Martial Arts school.

   (C) In front of a Chinese language school.

10. Which of the following statements is true?

    (A) The boy wants to buy a book about Chinese Martial Arts.

    (B) Tai-chi is good exercise for people of all ages.

    (C) The boy seems to know nothing about the place.

SECTION II   USAGE
Suggested time – 20 minutes/Questions 11-28

Directions: This section consists of a number of incomplete sentences. Each sentence has three answer choices. Select one word or phrase to fill in the blank to make the sentence complete both structurally and logically.

The questions are presented in four different ways: traditional characters, simplified characters, pinyin romanization and the Chinese phonetic alphabet (bopomofo). Zhuyin and pinyin of each question are posted on the Meizhou Chinese website. You can also listen to the questions on your CD.

11. 那場表演好看極___！

(A) 了
(B) 吧
(C) 嗎

11. 那场表演好看极___！

(A) 了
(B) 吧
(C) 吗

12. 中國棒球隊的球技___美國隊好！

(A) 給
(B) 要
(C) 比

12. 中国棒球队的球技___美国队好！

(A) 给
(B) 要
(C) 比

13. 奶奶給小狗___名字叫來福。

(A) 給
(B) 取
(C) 寫

13. 奶奶给小狗___名字叫来福。

(A) 给
(B) 取
(C) 写

14. 他上了初中___，成績就進步很多。
(A) 以後
(B) 後來
(C) 以前

14. 他上了初中___，成绩就进步很多。
(A) 以后
(B) 后来
(C) 以前

15. _____他上了高中，就更加用功了。
(A) 以後
(B) 以前
(C) 後來

15. _____他上了高中，就更加用功了。
(A) 以后
(B) 以前
(C) 后来

16. _____很晚了，我們回去吧！
(A) 已經
(B) 以後
(C) 曾經

16. _____很晚了，我们回去吧！
(A) 已经
(B) 以后
(C) 曾经

17. _____我很愛吃糖，_____不敢多吃。
   (A) 不但…而且
   (B) 雖然…可是
   (C) 因為…所以

18. 今年夏天的天氣，熱得讓人_____！
   (A) 不受了
   (B) 受不了
   (C) 受得了

19. 弟弟還小，很多事我都___著他！
   (A) 讓
   (B) 給
   (C) 替

20. 如果天氣不好，學校____取消比賽。
   (A) 難怪
   (B) 至少
   (C) 只能

21. 氣象報告說今天會下雨，____下雨
    了。
   (A) 果然
   (B) 忽然
   (C) 依然

22. 他每天____很早就起床。
   (A) 總共
   (B) 總是
   (C) 總算

17. _____我很愛吃糖，_____不敢多吃。
   (A) 不但…而且
   (B) 虽然…可是
   (C) 因为…所以

18. 今年夏天的天气，热得让人_____！
   (A) 不受了
   (B) 受不了
   (C) 受得了

19. 弟弟还小，很多事我都___着他！
   (A) 让
   (B) 给
   (C) 替

20. 如果天气不好，学校____取消比赛。
   (A) 难怪
   (B) 至少
   (C) 只能

21. 气象报告说今天会下雨，____下雨
    了。
   (A) 果然
   (B) 忽然
   (C) 依然

22. 他每天____很早就起床。
   (A) 总共
   (B) 总是
   (C) 总算

23. 我長大了要____老師。
    (A) 作
    (B) 當
    (C) 是

23. 我长大了要____老师。
    (A) 作
    (B) 当
    (C) 是

24. 一____可愛的鴨子在池子裡面玩耍。
    (A) 個
    (B) 群
    (C) 堆

24. 一____可爱的鸭子在池子里面玩耍。
    (A) 个
    (B) 群
    (C) 堆

25. 花木蘭___是個孝順的女兒，___是位
    勇敢的軍人。
    (A) 不但…而且
    (B) 雖然…如此
    (C) 儘管…卻

25. 花木兰___是个孝顺的女儿，___是位
    勇敢的军人。
    (A) 不但…而且
    (B) 虽然…如此
    (C) 尽管…却

26. 今年你___看了幾本書？
    (A) 總是
    (B) 總算
    (C) 總共

26. 今年你___看了几本书？
    (A) 总是
    (B) 总算
    (C) 总共

27. 花木蘭的朋友看見她穿著女裝出現，
    _____。
    (A) 驚慌失措
    (B) 大喊大叫
    (C) 大吃一驚

27. 花木兰的朋友看见她穿着女装出现，
    _____。
    (A) 惊慌失措
    (B) 大喊大叫
    (C) 大吃一惊

28. 我們_____。
    (A) 不要人在福中千萬不知福
    (B) 不要千萬人在福中不知福
    (C) 千萬不要人在福中不知福

28. 我们_____。
    (A) 不要人在福中千万不知福
    (B) 不要千万人在福中不知福
    (C) 千万不要人在福中不知福

SECTION III   READING COMPREHENSION
Suggested time – 20 minutes/ Questions 29 – 38

Directions: Read the following texts carefully. Each is followed by one or more questions or incomplete statements. Circle the best answer according to the text.

Questions 29-30

| 軍營重地 |
| 閒人免進 |

Questions 29-30

| 军营重地 |
| 闲人免进 |

29. Where will you see this sign?

(A) At a government building

(B) At a campground

(C) At a military base

30. What should you do when you see the sign?

(A) Take pictures

(B) Do not enter

(C) Stop talking

Question 31

| 中華少年武術館 |

Question 31

| 中华少年武术馆 |

31. This is a sign of the _____.

(A) Chinese Martial Arts Club for Youth

(B) Chinese Shao Lin Kung Fu Club

(C) Chinese Activity Club for Children

Question 32

青青：

　　《葉問》的電影碟片我買到了，葉大師的武功很高，這個電影好看極了。明天我帶去學校借給你看。

明明 上

Question 32

青青:

　　《叶问》的电影碟片我买到了，叶大师的武功很高，这个电影好看极了。明天我带去学校借给你看。

明明 上

32. According to this letter, which of the following statements is NOT true?
    (A)   The name of the movie is a person's name.
    (B)   Ming Ming will drop off the CD at Qing Qing's apartment / place.
    (C)   This is a movie about Chinese Martial Arts.

Questions 33-34

園林中學 中文電影週

星期六(4/2)：《跑吧!孩子》親情片
星期日(4/3)：《少林足球》武打片
晚上七點在大禮堂放映，門口售票。
詳情請上網：yuanlinschool.com

Questions 33-34

园林中学 中文电影周

星期六(4/2)：《跑吧! 孩子》亲情片
星期日(4/3)：《少林足球》武打片
晚上七点在大礼堂放映，门口售票。
详情请上网：yuanlinschool.com

33. Which of the following statements is NOT true?
    (A) It is a "Chinese Film Week" program.
    (B) This is a weekly Chinese film program.
    (C) The martial arts show is on Sunday.

34. Which of the following information is NOT on the flyer?
    (A) The names of the films
    (B) The location of the show
    (C) The price of the ticket

Questions 35-37

新書介紹

書名：《讀唐詩練功夫》
作者：任培豪、陳亞男
出版社：本事文化
說明：這是一本介紹一邊練中國功
　　　夫、一邊念唐詩的書。每個
　　　動作都有照片和文字的對照
　　　說明。三歲小孩可以跟著大
　　　人練，老少皆宜。

Questions 35-37

新书介绍

书名：《读唐诗练功夫》
作者：任培豪、陈亚男
出版社：本事文化
说明：这是一本介绍一边练中国功
　　　夫、一边念唐诗的书。每个
　　　动作都有照片和文字的对照
　　　说明。三岁小孩可以跟着大
　　　人练，老少皆宜。

35. What is on this poster？

    (A) A new book introduction.

    (B) An advertisement for a story book.

    (C) An advertisement for a poetry book.

36. Which of the following is NOT mentioned on the poster?

    (A) The price of this book.

    (B) The authors of this book.

    (C) The publisher of this book.

37. According to the information on the poster, which of the following statements is NOT true?

    (A) This book is good for kids as well as adults.

    (B) One can practice martial arts and recite poems at the same time.

    (C) One can watch the videos and practice.

Question 38

Question 38

在美國不但陸軍、海軍有女性，連空軍都有女軍人。美國政府在 2013 年公布，美國軍隊裡有 20 萬女軍人，其中有 69 位是將軍。

在美国不但陆军、海军有女性，连空军都有女军人。美国政府在 2013 年公布，美国军队里有 20 万女军人，其中有 69 位是将军。

38. Which of the following statements is true?

    (A) There are two hundred thousand female soldiers in the U.S. military.

    (B) There are 69 female generals in the U.S. Army.

    (C) There are 69 female generals in the U.S. Army and Navy combined.

II. AP Practice

1. Writing (E-mail Response)

Question 1 of 2: Read this e-mail from a friend and then type a response.

發件人:小華 郵件主題:當空軍 　我的夢想就是當軍人和開飛機，所以我準備進空軍學校，可是我媽媽不喜歡女孩子當軍人。我要怎麼說服她呢？請你告訴我。	发件人: 小华 邮件主题: 当空军 　我的梦想就是当军人和开飞机，所以我准备进空军学校，可是我妈妈不喜欢女孩子当军人。我要怎么说服她呢？请你告诉我。

2. Writing (Story Narration)

Question 2 of 2: The four pictures below present a story. Imagine you are writing this story to a friend. Narrate the complete story as shown in the pictures. Give your story a beginning, a middle, and an end. Please write the story on a separate sheet of paper or type it down on a computer.

III. Idioms/Frequently Used Phrases (Traditional)

You can listen to idioms, phrases, and questions on your CD.

英勇善戰	yīng yǒng shàn zhàn	to be brave and skillful in battles
體弱多病	tǐ ruò duō bìng	weak and often sick
家喻戶曉	jiā yù hù xiǎo	widely known
孝養父母	xiào yǎng fù mǔ	to take care of one's parents
女扮男裝	nǚ bàn nán zhuāng	a woman in men's clothing; a woman disguised as a man
幸福美滿	xìng fú měi mǎn	happy life

1. 木蘭從軍是一個在中國流傳了一千多年，＿＿＿＿＿＿＿＿的故事。

2. 當時的國王要和敵人打仗，木蘭的父親雖然＿＿＿＿＿＿＿＿，但是也被徵召了。

3. 花木蘭身強體健，她決定＿＿＿＿＿＿＿＿，代父從軍。

4. 花木蘭從軍十二年，她＿＿＿＿＿＿＿＿，常常打勝仗。

5. 戰爭結束以後，花木蘭決定趕回家鄉＿＿＿＿＿＿＿＿。

6. 最後，花木蘭和她的戰友賀靈將軍結婚了，過著＿＿＿＿＿＿＿＿的日子。

III. Idioms/Frequently Used Phrases (Simplified)

You can listen to idioms, phrases, and questions on your CD.

英勇善战	yīng yǒng shàn zhàn	to be brave and skillful in battles
体弱多病	tǐ ruò duō bìng	weak and often sick
家喻户晓	jiā yù hù xiǎo	widely known
孝养父母	xiào yǎng fù mǔ	to take care of one's parents
女扮男装	nǚ bàn nán zhuāng	a woman in men's clothing; a woman disguised as a man
幸福美满	xìng fú měi mǎn	happy life

1. 木兰从军是一个在中国流传了一千多年，_____的故事。

2. 当时的国王要和敌人打仗，木兰的父亲虽然_____，但是也被征召了。

3. 花木兰身强体健，她决定_____，代父从军。

4. 花木兰从军十二年，她_____，常常打胜仗。

5. 战争结束以后，花木兰决定赶回家乡_____。

6. 最后，花木兰和她的战友贺灵将军结婚了，过着_____的日子。

IV. Vocabulary/Phrase Review

Please translate the following words/phrases into Chinese.

Lesson 8: (based on the text book   p.129)

English	Chinese	English	Chinese
courage		one piece of (clothing or matter)	
brave		altogether; total	
to fight a war or battle		president (of a country)	
veterans		well-being; blissfulness; happiness	
to be soldier; to join the army		although; even if; in spite of	
to bear; to endure; to tolerate			
to get hurt; injured			
female; feminine			
a commanding officer; a senior official, a superior			
Washington			
to concede; to make way for			

I. SAT Practice: 1. Listening (10) 2. Usage (18) 3. Reading Comprehension (10)

II. AP Practice: 1. Writing (E-mail Response) 2. Writing (Story Narration)

III. Idioms/Frequently Used Phrases

IV. Vocabulary/Phrase Review

I. SAT Practice
SECTION I LISTENING   Approximate time – 10 minutes

PART A
Directions: In this part of the test, you will hear some short questions, statements, or commands, as well as responses, in Mandarin Chinese. Each question, statement, or command is followed by three responses, designated by letters (A), (B), and (C). You will hear the recording only one time. You will only hear, but not see, the recording materials. Therefore, you must listen very attentively. Select the best response and circle the answer.
Now listen to the recording.

PART B
Directions: You will now hear a series of short conversations. After each conversation, you will answer one or more questions about it. You will hear the conversations only once. You will only hear, but not see, the conversation materials. Therefore, you must listen very attentively. Select and circle your answer choice to each question. You will have fifteen seconds to answer each question.
Now listen to the first conversation.

Circle the answer.

Questions 1-4

1. (A)   (B)   (C)

2. (A)   (B)   (C)

3. (A)   (B)   (C)

4. (A)   (B)   (C)

Question 5

5. What is this conversation about?
  (A) The building
  (B) The sculpture
  (C) The campus

Questions 6-7

6. Where would this conversation most likely take place?
  (A) On the first floor
  (B) On the second floor
  (C) On the third floor

7. Where do they plan to visit at the end?
   (A) The gift shop on the first floor
   (B) The exhibit hall on the third floor
   (C) The exhibit hall on the second floor

Question 8

8. According to the conversation, what will they do?
   (A) They will leave after three days.
   (B) They will wait for a couple of days.
   (C) They are going to do something different.

Questions 9-10

9. When is the Red Earth Festival?
   (A) In June, annually.
   (B) In June, every other year.
   (C) In May, annually.

10. What is this conversation about?
   (A) Supporting Indian activities.
   (B) Helping Indians preserve their culture.
   (C) The date of the festival.

SECTION II   USAGE
Suggested time – 20 minutes/Questions 11-28

Directions: This section consists of a number of incomplete sentences. Each sentence has three answer choices. Select one word or phrase to fill in the blank to make the sentence complete both structurally and logically.
The questions are presented in four different ways: traditional characters, simplified characters, pinyin romanization and the Chinese phonetic alphabet (bopomofo). Zhuyin and pinyin of each question are posted on the Meizhou Chinese website. You can also listen to the questions on your CD.

11. 那是一_____大理石的雕像。

   (A) 台
   (B) 座
   (C) 塊

11. 那是一_____大理石的雕像。

   (A) 台
   (B) 座
   (C) 块

12. 哥哥____都非常照顧我。

   (A) 全部
   (B) 一來
   (C) 一向

12. 哥哥____都非常照顾我。

   (A) 全部
   (B) 一来
   (C) 一向

13. 印地安人_____大地是神聖的。

   (A) 認爲
   (B) 以為
   (C) 認識

13. 印地安人_____大地是神圣的。

   (A) 认为
   (B) 以为
   (C) 认识

14. 到了夏天，白天就_____了。
   (A) 越來越冷
   (B) 越來越多
   (C) 越來越長

14. 到了夏天，白天就_____了。
   (A) 越来越冷
   (B) 越来越多
   (C) 越来越长

15. 印地安人被歐洲人___東部趕___
   西部。
   (A) 從…到
   (B) 由…來
   (C) 向…去

15. 印地安人被欧洲人___东部赶___
   西部。
   (A) 从…到
   (B) 由…来
   (C) 向…去

16. 我回家____，第一件事就是洗手
   吃點心。
   (A) 之前
   (B) 之後
   (C) 後來

16. 我回家____，第一件事就是洗手
   吃点心。
   (A) 之前
   (B) 之后
   (C) 后来

17. 美國的移民，最早是從東岸___西岸
    發展。
    (A) 向
    (B) 轉
    (C) 走

18. 他____有錢_____去買書。
    (A) 剛…要
    (B) 一…就
    (C) 只…就

19. 我們都___注意安全。
    (A) 叫
    (B) 得
    (C) 用

20. 他去年五月份就_____畢業了。
    (A) 已經
    (B) 剛才
    (C) 曾經

21. 這個玩具很可愛，___有很多功能。
    (A) 並且
    (B) 況且
    (C) 還是

22. 天黑了，他到家了_____？
    (A) 吧
    (B) 嗎
    (C) 呢

17. 美国的移民，最早是从东岸___西岸
    发展。
    (A) 向
    (B) 转
    (C) 走

18. 他____有钱_____去买书。
    (A) 刚…要
    (B) 一…就
    (C) 只…就

19. 我们都___注意安全。
    (A) 叫
    (B) 得
    (C) 用

20. 他去年五月份就_____毕业了。
    (A) 已经
    (B) 刚才
    (C) 曾经

21. 这个玩具很可爱，___有很多功能。
    (A) 并且
    (B) 况且
    (C) 还是

22. 天黑了，他到家了_____？
    (A) 吧
    (B) 吗
    (C) 呢

23. 做這道題的方法_____一種。
    (A) 只有
    (B) 只要
    (C) 除非

24. 我們是從法國移民來美國___。
    (A) 得
    (B) 地
    (C) 的

25. 這台電腦_____是我想要的。
    (A) 正好
    (B) 可以
    (C) 正要

26. _____他經常運動，所以他身體很
    健康。
    (A) 而且
    (B) 應該
    (C) 因為

27. 他們家_____住在這個小村莊。
    (A) 分分秒秒
    (B) 長長久久
    (C) 世世代代

28. 我_____。
    (A) 要去爺爺家陪他明天
    (B) 明天要去爺爺家陪他
    (C) 要去爺爺家明天陪他

23. 做这道题的方法_____一种。
    (A) 只有
    (B) 只要
    (C) 除非

24. 我们是从法国移民来美国___。
    (A) 得
    (B) 地
    (C) 的

25. 这台电脑_____是我想要的。
    (A) 正好
    (B) 可以
    (C) 正要

26. _____他经常运动，所以他身体很
    健康。
    (A) 而且
    (B) 应该
    (C) 因为

27. 他们家_____住在这个小村庄。
    (A) 分分秒秒
    (B) 长长久久
    (C) 世世代代

28. 我_____。
    (A) 要去爷爷家陪他明天
    (B) 明天要去爷爷家陪他
    (C) 要去爷爷家明天陪他

SECTION III READING COMPREHENSION
Suggested time – 20 minutes/ Questions 29 – 38

Directions: Read the following texts carefully. Each is followed by one or more questions or incomplete statements. Circle the best answer according to the text.

Question 29

全美旅行社
華盛頓一日遊
機場接送，中文導遊。
電話：800-888-8888

Question 29

全美旅行社
华盛顿一日游
机场接送，中文导游。
电话: 800-888-8888

29. This is an advertisement for_____.

(A) A hotel

(B) A taxi company

(C) A travel agency

Question 30

園林中學學生會選舉

請投票給

會長候選人

✔ 王明明

Question 30

园林中学学生会选举

请投票给

会长候选人

✔ 王明明

30. Which of the following statements is true?

(A) This is a student council election flyer.

(B) This is a recruitment flyer.

(C) Wang Ming-Ming will run for vice president.

五年級上課時間表					
時間/日期	星期一	星期二	星期三	星期四	星期五
08：10 - 09：10	數學	數學	數學	數學	數學
09：10 - 10：10	英文	英文	英文	英文	英文
10：10 - 10：30	上午休息時間				
10：30 - 11：30	科學	常識	科學	常識	常識
11：30 - 12：30	常識	音樂	數學	音樂	英文
12：30 - 13：10	午餐時間				
13：10 - 14：50	體育	數學	體育	英文	美術

Questions 31-32

五年级上课时间表					
时间/日期	星期一	星期二	星期三	星期四	星期五
08：10 - 09：10	数学	数学	数学	数学	数学
09：10 - 10：10	英文	英文	英文	英文	英文
10：10 - 10：30	上午休息时间				
10：30 - 11：30	科学	常识	科学	常识	常识
11：30 - 12：30	常识	音乐	数学	音乐	英文
12：30 - 13：10	午餐时间				
13：10 - 14：50	体育	数学	体育	英文	美术

31. Which of the following courses meets for the longest time every week?

    (A) Science and Math

    (B) Math and English

    (C) English and Science

32. Which days of the week have two math classes?

    (A) Monday, Tuesday

    (B) Tuesday, Wednesday

    (C) Tuesday, Thursday

Questions 33-34

華盛頓的美國印地安人博物館有三個展覽區：分別是「我們的世界」、「我們的人民」、「我們的生活」。裡面收藏了印第安人從古到今的陶器、紡織品和雕刻品。博物館除了聖誕節之外，每天開放。

Questions 33-34

华盛顿的美国印地安人博物馆有三个展览区：分别是"我们的世界"、"我们的人民"、"我们的生活"。里面收藏了印第安人从古到今的陶器、纺织品和雕刻品。博物馆除了圣诞节之外，每天开放。

33. Which collections are featured in the Indian Museum at Washington DC?

    (A) Indian sculpture

    (B) American paintings

    (C) Early American furniture from The Mayflower

34. Which of the following statements is INCORRECT?

    (A) There are areas in the Indian museum that display Indian life.

    (B) The Indian museum introduces the Indian World.

    (C) The Indian museum is open all year round.

Questions 35-36

1851 年以後，美國政府讓印地安人搬到保留區去生活。保留區的天氣不好，土地不好，生產不出食物來，所以印地安人還是很窮。現在美國大約有 310 個印地安人保留區，加州的最多。

Questions 35-36

1851 年以后，美国政府让印地安人搬到保留区去生活。保留区的天气不好，土地不好，生产不出食物来，所以印地安人还是很穷。现在美国大约有 310 个印地安人保留区，加州的最多。

35. Which of the following statements is NOT true about Indian Reservations?
   (A) There is enough food.
   (B) Weather is bad.
   (C) Reservation lands are not good for farming.

36. Which of the following statements is INCORRECT?
   (A) The American government made Indians move to reservations.
   (B) California has a few Indian Reservations.
   (C) Indians on reservations are poor.

Questions 37-38

我們要愛護環境，也就是說要綠化環境。比如垃圾分類、廢物回收、儘量少開車，並且要多種樹，讓城市綠化起來。

Questions 37-38

我们要爱护环境，也就是说要绿化环境。比如垃圾分类、废物回收、尽量少开车，并且要多种树，让城市绿化起来。

37. According to the text, how should people protect the environment?
   (A) Grow more green plants.
   (B) Make the environment clean.
   (C) Make the environment convenient for driving.

38. Which of the following statements is NOT mentioned?
   (A) Drive as less often as possible.
   (B) Water plants if necessary.
   (C) Recycle and sort garbage into proper categories.

II.   AP Practice

1. Writing (E-mail Response)

Question 1 of 2: Read this e-mail from a friend and then type a response.

發件人:小華
郵件主題:美洲印地安人

　　我要寫一篇關於美洲印地安人的讀書報告。你知道印地安人在美洲有多久的歷史嗎?他們在美國算是少數民族嗎?少數民族要用什麼方法使自己強大呢?

发件人: 小华
邮件主题: 美洲印地安人

　　我要写一篇关于美洲印地安人的读书报告。你知道印地安人在美洲有多久的历史吗? 他们在美国算是少数民族吗? 少数民族要用什么方法使自己强大呢?

2. Writing (Story Narration)

Question 2 of 2: The four pictures below present a story. Imagine you are writing this story to a friend. Narrate the complete story as shown in the pictures. Give your story a beginning, a middle, and an end. Please write the story on a separate sheet of paper or type it down on a computer.

III. Idioms/Frequently Used Phrases (Traditional)

You can listen to idioms, phrases, and questions on your CD.

世世代代	shì shì dài dài	from generation to generation
一望無際	yí wàng wú jì	stretching far off into the distance and out of sight
山明水秀	shān míng shuǐ xiù	beautiful mountain and river; picturesque scenery
貧窮落後	pín qióng luò hòu	poor and fall behind
長槍利劍	cháng qiāng lì jiàn	long guns and sharp swords
自立自強	zì lì zì qiáng	self-reliance

1. 很久以前，美洲大陸就是印地安人＿＿＿＿＿＿＿居住的地方。

2. 印地安人愛護自然，他們在這片＿＿＿＿＿＿＿、＿＿＿＿＿＿＿的

 土地上，快快樂樂的生活著。

3. 1495 年，歐洲人來了，他們用＿＿＿＿＿＿＿，打打殺殺，要趕走印地

 安人。

4. 最後，歐洲移民佔據了整個美洲，印地安人住進了山區，過著

 ＿＿＿＿＿＿＿的生活。

5. 印地安人要＿＿＿＿＿＿＿，知識和選票才是力量。

III. Idioms/Frequently Used Phrases (Simplified)

You can listen to idioms, phrases, and questions on your CD.

世世代代	shì shì dài dài	from generation to generation
一望无际	yí wàng wú jì	stretching far off into the distance and out of sight
山明水秀	shān míng shuǐ xiù	beautiful mountain and river; picturesque scenery
贫穷落后	pín qióng luò hòu	poor and fall behind
长枪利剑	cháng qiāng lì jiàn	long guns and sharp swords
自强自立	zì qiáng zì lì	self-reliance

1. 很久以前，美洲大陆就是印地安人_____居住的地方。

2. 印地安人爱护自然，他们在这片_____、_____的
    土地上，快快乐乐的生活着。

3. 1495 年，欧洲人来了，他们用_____，打打杀杀，要赶走印地
    安人。

4. 最后，欧洲移民占据了整个美洲，印地安人住进了山区，过着
    _____的生活。

5. 印地安人要_____，知识和选票才是力量。

IV. Vocabulary/Phrase Review

Please translate the following words/phrases into Chinese.

Lesson 9: (based on the text book p.129-130)

English	Chinese	English	Chinese
to visit (a place); to tour		to stay	
history		to emigrate; immigrant	
museum		election	
restaurant		ballot	
science		strength; force	
newly-built			
American Indians			
getting better all the time			
ancient history			
to keep			
ancestor; ancestry; grandparents			

I. SAT Practice: 1. Listening (10) 2. Usage (18) 3. Reading Comprehension (10)

II. AP Practice: 1. Writing (E-mail Response) 2. Writing (Story Narration)

III. Idioms/Frequently Used Phrases

IV. Vocabulary/Phrase Review

I. SAT Practice
SECTION I   LISTENING   Approximate time – 10 minutes

PART A
Directions: In this part of the test, you will hear some short questions, statements, or commands, as well as responses, in Mandarin Chinese. Each question, statement, or command is followed by three responses, designated by letters (A), (B), and (C). You will hear the recording only one time. You will only hear, but not see, the recording materials. Therefore, you must listen very attentively. Select the best response and circle the answer.
Now listen to the recording.

Circle the answer.

Questions 1-4

1. (A)   (B)   (C)

2. (A)   (B)   (C)

3. (A)   (B)   (C)

4. (A)   (B)   (C)

PART B
Directions: You will now hear a series of short conversations. After each conversation, you will answer one or more questions about it. You will hear the conversations only once. You will only hear, but not see, the conversation materials. Therefore, you must listen very attentively. Select and circle your answer choice to each question. You will have fifteen seconds to answer each question.
Now listen to the first conversation.

Question 5

5. When is the girl's turn?
   (A) Two days after tomorrow
   (B) The day after tomorrow
   (C) Tomorrow

Question 6

6. How does the girl get to the library?
   (A) She just follows the people in front of her.
   (B) She just follows the teacher.
   (C) She just follows the boy.

Question 7

7. What does the boy suggest the girl to buy?

    (A) Bamboo clappers

    (B) Bamboo plates

    (C) Bamboo sheets

Questions 8-9

8. What is this conversation about?

    (A) How to do "Shu Lai Pao"

    (B) How to prepare an end of the school year party

    (C) How to show gratitude towards a teacher

9. What is the boy's opinion about this issue?

    (A) He doesn't have a preference

    (B) He agrees with the majority

    (C) He agrees with the minority

Question 10

10. What is this conversation about?

    (A) The benefits of doing homework during the summer.

    (B) The best way to do homework during the summer.

    (C) If students should do homework during the summer.

SECTION II   USAGE
Suggested time – 20 minutes/Questions 11-28

Directions: This section consists of a number of incomplete sentences. Each sentence has three answer choices. Select one word or phrase to fill in the blank to make the sentence complete both structurally and logically.

The questions are presented in four different ways: traditional characters, simplified characters, pinyin romanization and the Chinese phonetic alphabet (bopomofo). Zhuyin and pinyin of each question are posted on the Meizhou Chinese website. You can also listen to the questions on your CD.

11. 媽媽生病了，我和妹妹___照顧她。

    (A) 輪流
    (B) 轉動
    (C) 轉換

12. 全校的同樂會表演，___一年級學生
    開始。
    (A) 跟
    (B) 起
    (C) 由

13. 弟弟__著我去學校上課。

    (A) 同
    (B) 跟
    (C) 向

14. 學校的體育場就在教室的_____。
    (A) 以後
    (B) 後面
    (C) 後來

15. 爸爸____工作努力____，還很照顧
    家。
    (A) 除了…以外
    (B) 雖然…可是
    (C) 如果…還是

16. 這道數學題很難，___我做出來了。
    (A) 即使
    (B) 況且
    (C) 但是

11. 妈妈生病了，我和妹妹___照顾她。

    (A) 轮流
    (B) 转动
    (C) 转换

12. 全校的同乐会表演，___一年级学生
    开始。
    (A) 跟
    (B) 起
    (C) 由

13. 弟弟__着我去学校上课。

    (A) 同
    (B) 跟
    (C) 向

14. 学校的体育场就在教室的_____。
    (A) 以后
    (B) 后面
    (C) 后来

15. 爸爸____工作努力____，还很照顾
    家。
    (A) 除了…以外
    (B) 虽然…可是
    (C) 如果…还是

16. 这道数学题很难，___我做出来了。
    (A) 即使
    (B) 况且
    (C) 但是

17. 他買了好幾___西裝。
    (A) 條
    (B) 個
    (C) 套

18. 這家飯店生意很好，我們___等了一個
    鐘頭，還沒輪到我們。
    (A) 已經
    (B) 仍然
    (C) 然後

19. 唐僧___走到那裡，孫悟空___會跟著
    他。
    (A) 不只…都
    (B) 不論…都
    (C) 不管…還

20. 我___睡覺，他___打電話來了。
    (A) 正要…就
    (B) 曾經…也
    (C) 一直…就

21. 這部電影講的是一___白馬和牠的
    主人的故事。
    (A) 個
    (B) 匹
    (C) 頭

22. 孫悟空___就成了一隻小飛蟲。
    (A) 搖身一變
    (B) 一成不變
    (C) 變化多端

17. 他买了好几___西装。
    (A) 条
    (B) 个
    (C) 套

18. 这家饭店生意很好，我们___等了一个
    钟头，还没轮到我们。
    (A) 已经
    (B) 仍然
    (C) 然后

19. 唐僧___走到那里，孙悟空___会跟着
    他。
    (A) 不只…都
    (B) 不论…都
    (C) 不管…还

20. 我___睡觉，他___打电话来了。
    (A) 正要…就
    (B) 曾经…也
    (C) 一直…就

21. 这部电影讲的是一___白马和它的
    主人的故事。
    (A) 个
    (B) 匹
    (C) 头

22. 孙悟空___就成了一只小飞虫。
    (A) 摇身一变
    (B) 一成不变
    (C) 变化多端

23. 她想要當學生代表，＿＿被選上了。
    (A) 依然
    (B) 到底
    (C) 果然

24. 昨天他＿＿買了一套西裝，今天＿＿穿
    去上班了。
    (A) 只…都
    (B) 才…卻
    (C) 剛…就

25. ＿＿＿今天請客，所以媽媽做了很多
    菜。
    (A) 因此
    (B) 因為
    (C) 如果

26. ＿＿冬天很冷，他＿＿天天游泳。
    (A) 依然…還是
    (B) 果然…還是
    (C) 雖然…還是

27. 媽媽做的菜＿＿＿＿比餐館好吃。
    (A) 何必
    (B) 其實
    (C) 特地

28. 我＿＿＿＿＿＿＿＿＿＿＿＿＿＿。
    (A) 明天答應和他一起去爬山
    (B) 答應和他一起去爬山明天
    (C) 答應明天和他一起去爬山

23. 她想要当学生代表，＿＿被选上了。
    (A) 依然
    (B) 到底
    (C) 果然

24. 昨天他＿＿买了一套西装，今天＿＿穿
    去上班了。
    (A) 只…都
    (B) 才…却
    (C) 刚…就

25. ＿＿＿今天请客，所以妈妈做了很多
    菜。
    (A) 因此
    (B) 因为
    (C) 如果

26. ＿＿冬天很冷，他＿＿天天游泳。
    (A) 依然…还是
    (B) 果然…还是
    (C) 虽然…还是

27. 妈妈做的菜＿＿＿＿比餐馆好吃。
    (A) 何必
    (B) 其实
    (C) 特地

28. 我＿＿＿＿＿＿＿＿＿＿＿＿＿＿。
    (A) 明天答应和他一起去爬山
    (B) 答应和他一起去爬山明天
    (C) 答应明天和他一起去爬山

SECTION III   READING COMPREHENSION
Suggested time – 20 minutes/ Questions 29 – 38

Directions: Read the following texts carefully. Each is followed by one or more questions or incomplete statements. Circle the best answer according to the text.

Question 29

結業同樂會
由此進 ➡

Question 29

结业同乐会
由此进 ➡

29. Which event is this sign giving directions to?

(A) A class party for the first day of school

(B) A class party for the end of the school year

(C) A class party for the awards ceremony

Question 30

王海雲漫畫集

《西遊記》

第一集

中英文版

中華出版社

Question 30

王海云漫画集

《西游记》

第一集

中英文版

中华出版社

30. Which of the following statements is true?

(A) This is a comic book.

(B) This is book two in this series.

(C) This is a Chinese storybook.

Question 31

Question 31

> 媽媽：
>
> 　我到友友家了，請放心！友友的爺爺指導我們練習，明天的表演一定成功。請您下班後就來接我，謝謝！
>
> 　　　　　兒子中中　敬上

> 妈妈：
>
> 　我到友友家了，请放心！友友的爷爷指导我们练习，明天的表演一定成功。请您下班后就来接我，谢谢！
>
> 　　　　　儿子中中　敬上

31. Which one of the following statements is INCORRECT?

(A) Zhong Zhong's mother is at work.

(B) Zhong Zhong sent this letter from his home.

(C) You You's grandpa will be their coach.

Questions 32-34

Questions 32-34

> 　為了準備今年母親節的園遊會，明明的爸爸寫了一篇數來寶做為歡迎詞。校長很喜歡，就讓幼稚園到五年級，每年級派兩位學生上台表演。他們一邊說唱，一邊用竹板、筷子、鈴鼓打拍子，十分逗趣！台下的媽媽們都笑得合不攏嘴。

> 　为了准备今年母亲节的园游会，明明的爸爸写了一篇数来宝做为欢迎词。校长很喜欢，就让幼稚园到五年级，每年级派两位学生上台表演。他们一边说唱，一边用竹板、筷子、铃鼓打拍子，十分逗趣！台下的妈妈们都笑得合不拢嘴。

32. Who did the eulogy for Mother's Day celebration?

(A) The principal

(B) A student

(C) Ming-Ming's father.

33. How many students performed the "Shu Lai Bao"?

(A) 10

(B) 12

(C) 6

34. Which of the following props were NOT used by the students?

(A) Jingle bells

(B) Chopsticks

(C) Bamboo clappers

Questions 35-36

數來寶

　　千歡迎，萬歡迎，歡迎大家的光臨！園遊會，表演多，熱鬧登場等著您！母愛深，難以報，一點一滴獻給您呀，獻給您！

（節錄改寫自黃麗娟感恩相聲劇本）

Questions 35-36

数来宝

　　千欢迎，万欢迎，欢迎大家的光临！园游会，表演多，热闹登场等着您！母爱深，难以报，一点一滴献给您呀，献给您！

（节录改写自黄丽娟感恩相声剧本）

35. What is this text talking about?

　(A) Saying thanks to mothers.

　(B) Saying thanks to teachers.

　(C) Saying thanks to friends.

36. Which of the following is NOT mentioned in the text?

　(A) The dance

　(B) The performance

　(C) The fair

Questions 37-38

　　《西遊記》是講唐僧帶著孫悟空、豬八戒和沙僧三個徒弟，去印度取經的故事。他們一路上遇到許多危險，終於取得佛經回到中國。這本小說被翻譯成英文、法文、西班牙文等文字之前，已經有了日文版。

Questions 37-38

　　《西游记》是讲唐僧带着孙悟空、猪八戒和沙僧三个徒弟，去印度取经的故事。他们一路上遇到许多危险，终于取得佛经回到中国。这本小说被翻译成英文、法文、西班牙文等文字之前，已经有了日文版。

37. Which of the following statements is NOT true ?

　(A) Tang Seng and his three disciples made a journey to Thailand.

　(B) The purpose of the Journey was to obtain the Buddhist Sutras.

　(C) Sun Wu-Kong was one of Tang Seng's disciples.

38. According to the paragraph, this book was first translated into _____

　(A) English

　(B) Japanese

　(C) French

II. AP Practice
1. Writing (E-mail Response)

Question 1 of 2: Read this e-mail from a friend and then type a response.

發件人：小華
郵件主題：西遊記

　　我們班要演一段《西遊記》的故事，我不知道要扮演唐僧還是孫悟空。請你給我一些建議好嗎？
謝謝！

发件人：小华
邮件主题：西游记

　　我们班要演一段《西游记》的故事，我不知道要扮演唐僧还是孙悟空。请你给我一些建议好吗？
谢谢！

2. Writing (Story Narration)

Question 2 of 2: The four pictures below present a story. Imagine you are writing this story to a friend. Narrate the complete story as shown in the pictures. Give your story a beginning, a middle, and an end. Please write the story on a separate sheet of paper or type it down on a computer.

III. Idioms/Frequently Used Phrases (Traditional)

You can listen to idioms, phrases, and questions on your CD.

千山萬水	qiān shān wàn shuǐ	thousands of miles
妖魔鬼怪	yāo mó guǐ guài	demons and ghosts
盡心盡力	jìn xīn jìn lì	dedicated
肩負重任	jiān fù zhòng rèn	to shoulder a heavy responsibility
通天本事	tōng tiān běn shì	superior ability and skill
大功告成	dà gōng gào chéng	to have accomplished a mission

1. 唐僧必須經過＿＿＿＿＿＿＿＿＿到西天取經。

2. 往西天取經的路上有很多＿＿＿＿＿＿＿＿，是一段危險艱難的旅途。

3. 孫悟空有著＿＿＿＿＿＿＿＿，幫助唐僧收了豬八戒和沙和尚做徒弟。

4. 孫悟空、豬八戒和沙和尚都知道自己＿＿＿＿＿＿＿＿，必須保護師父。

5. 他們＿＿＿＿＿＿＿＿保護唐僧，結果取到經，而且＿＿＿＿＿＿＿＿

地回到中國。

III. Idioms/Frequently Used Phrases (Simplified)

You can listen to idioms, phrases, and questions on your CD.

千山万水	qiān shān wàn shuǐ	thousands of miles
妖魔鬼怪	yāo mó guǐ guài	demons and ghosts
尽心尽力	jìn xīn jìn lì	dedicated
肩负重任	jiān fù zhòng rèn	to shoulder a heavy responsibility
通天本事	tōng tiān běn shì	superior ability and skill
大功告成	dà gōng gào chéng	to have accomplished a mission

1. 唐僧必须经过_____到西天取经。

2. 往西天取经的路上有很多_____，是一段危险艰难的旅途。

3. 孙悟空有着_____，帮助唐僧收了猪八戒和沙和尚做徒弟。

4. 孙悟空、猪八戒和沙和尚都知道自己_____，必须保护师父。

5. 他们_____保护唐僧，结果取到经，而且_____

   地回到中国。

IV. Vocabulary/Phrase Review

Please translate the following words/phrases into Chinese.

Lesson 10: (based on the text book   p.130)

English	Chinese	English	Chinese
to act; to perform		to the greatest extent	
to hurry; to hasten; at once		except for; besides; other than	
reason		to need; demand; a need or demand	
to take turns		facial expression	
to ride a horse		to change	
very slow			
monster; goblin; demon			
ghosts and monsters; evil spirits; a goblin			
to obliterate			
to give an opinion			
to progress			

	Lesson 1	Lesson 2	Lesson 3	Lesson 4	Lesson 5	Lesson 6	Lesson 7	Lesson 8	Lesson 9	Lesson 10
1.	B	B	C	B	A	A	A	A	A	C
2.	A	B	A	A	C	B	B	B	B	A
3.	B	A	B	C	B	A	A	B	C	C
4.	C	A	C	A	A	C	A	C	A	B
5.	A	C	A	A	C	C	A	C	B	B
6.	C	B	A	B	B	A	C	A	A	B
7.	C	C	A	B	A	B	A	C	A	A
8.	A	B	B	A	C	C	A	A	B	C
9.	C	B	C	C	A	A	A	B	A	A
10.	B	C	B	A	B	B	C	B	B	B
11.	B	C	C	B	C	C	A	A	B	A
12.	C	A	A	B	A	A	B	C	C	C
13.	C	C	C	A	C	B	C	B	A	B
14.	A	A	B	B	B	C	B	A	C	B
15.	B	B	A	A	A	C	A	C	A	A
16.	B	B	C	B	A	A	C	A	B	C
17.	A	B	B	C	B	B	A	B	A	C
18.	B	A	B	B	B	A	B	B	B	A
19.	B	C	A	A	A	C	B	A	B	B
20.	C	C	C	C	A	A	A	C	A	A
21.	A	A	B	A	B	A	C	A	A	B
22.	C	B	A	C	C	B	A	B	B	A
23.	B	A	C	A	C	C	C	B	A	C
24.	A	B	A	C	C	A	C	B	C	C
25.	C	C	C	B	B	B	B	A	A	B
26.	B	C	B	C	B	C	C	C	C	C
27.	A	B	A	C	C	B	B	C	C	B
28.	A	C	B	C	A	B	A	C	B	C
29.	C	A	C	C	B	C	C	C	C	B
30.	B	C	B	C	B	A	C	B	A	A
31.	A	C	A	B	A	C	C	A	B	B
32	C	B	C	B	A	B	A	B	B	C
33.	C	A	A	C	C	A	C	B	A	B
34.	A	A	B	A	B	B	A	C	C	A
35.	A	C	B	B	B	B	B	A	A	A
36.	B	B	B	C	C	A	A	A	B	A
37.	A	B	C	A	A	A	B	C	A	A
38.	A	B	A	C	B	C	A	A	B	B